B

Contents

B CONTENTS

CONTENTS

PAGE

PAGE

B

Use of guidance

THE APPROVED DOCUMENTS

This document is one of a series that has been approved and issued by the Secretary of State for the purpose of providing practical guidance with respect to the requirements of Schedule 1 to and Regulation 7 of the Building Regulations 2010 (SI 2010/2214) for England and Wales.

At the back of this document is a list of all the documents that have been approved and issued by the Secretary of State for this purpose.

The Approved Documents are intended to provide guidance for some of the more common building situations. However, there may well be alternative ways of achieving compliance with the requirements.

Thus there is no obligation to adopt any particular solution contained in an Approved Document if you prefer to meet the relevant requirement in some other way.

Other requirements

The guidance contained in an Approved Document relates only to the particular requirements of the Regulations which that document addresses. The building work will also have to comply with the Requirements of any other relevant paragraphs in Schedule 1 to the Regulations.

There are Approved Documents which give guidance on each of the other requirements in Schedule 1 and on Regulation 7.

LIMITATION ON REQUIREMENTS

In accordance with Regulation 8, the requirements in Parts A to D, F to K, N and P (except for paragraphs H2 and J7) of Schedule 1 to the Building Regulations do not require anything to be done except for the purpose of securing reasonable standards of health and safety for persons in or about buildings (and any others who may be affected by buildings or matters connected with buildings). This is one of the categories of purpose for which Building Regulations may be made.

Paragraphs H2 and J7 are excluded from Regulation 8 because they deal directly with prevention of the contamination of water. Parts E and M (which deal, respectively, with resistance to the passage of sound, and access to and use of buildings) are excluded from Regulation 8 because they address the welfare and convenience of building users. Part L is excluded from Regulation 8 because it addresses the conservation of fuel and power. All these matters are amongst the purposes, other than health and safety, that may be addressed by Building Regulations.

MATERIALS AND WORKMANSHIP

Any building work which is subject to the requirements imposed by schedule 1 to the Building Regulations shall be carried out in accordance with regulation 7. Guidance on meeting these requirements on materials and workmanship is contained in the Approved Document to support regulation 7.

Building Regulations are made for specific purposes, primarily the health and safety, welfare and convenience of people and for energy conservation. Standards and other technical specifications may provide relevant guidance to the extent that they relate to these considerations. However, they may also address other aspects of performance or matters which, although they relate to health and safety etc., are not covered by the Building Regulations.

When an Approved Document makes reference to a named standard, the relevant version of the standard to which it refers is the one listed at the end of the publication. However, if this version has been revised or updated by the issuing standards body, the new version may be used as a source of guidance provided it continues to address the relevant requirements of the Regulations.

Independent certification schemes

There are many UK product certification schemes. Such schemes certify compliance with the requirements of a recognised document which is appropriate to the purpose for which the material is to be used. Materials which are not so certified may still conform to a relevant standard.

Many certification bodies which approve such schemes are accredited by United Kingdom Accreditation Service (UKAS).

Since the fire performance of a product, component or structure is dependent upon satisfactory site installation and maintenance, independent schemes of certification and accreditation of installers and maintenance firms of such will provide confidence in the appropriate standard of workmanship being provided.

Building Control Bodies may accept the certification of products, components, materials or structures under such schemes as evidence of compliance with the relevant standard. Similarly, Building Control Bodies may accept the certification of the installation or maintenance of products, components, materials or structures under such schemes as evidence of compliance with the relevant standard. Nonetheless, a Building Control Body will wish to establish, in advance of the work, that any such scheme is adequate for the purposes of the Building Regulations.

Technical specifications

Building Regulations are made for specific purposes, such as health and safety, energy conservation and the welfare and convenience of people. Standards and technical approvals are relevant guidance to the extent that they relate to these considerations. However, they may also address other aspects of performance such as serviceability, or aspects which, although they relate to health and safety, are not covered by the Regulations.

When an Approved Document makes reference to a named standard, the relevant version of the standard is the one listed at the end of the publication. However, if this version of the standard has been revised or updated by the issuing standards body, the new version may be used as a source of guidance provided it continues to address the relevant requirements of the Regulations.

The appropriate use of a product which complies with a European Technical Approval as defined in the Construction Products Directive will meet the relevant requirements.

The Department intends to issue periodic amendments to its Approved Documents to reflect emerging harmonised European Standards. Where a national standard is to be replaced by a European harmonised standard, there will be a co-existence period during which either standard may be referred to. At the end of the co-existence period the national standard will be withdrawn.

INTERACTION WITH OTHER LEGISLATION

Houses in multiple occupation

This guidance may also be applicable to the design and construction of dwellings which are considered to be 'houses in multiple occupation' (HMOs), as defined in the Housing Act 2004, providing there are no more than six residents in any self-contained dwelling. The licensing of HMOs is typically overseen by the Local Authority who may require additional precautions over and above this guidance. Technical guidance on the assessment of hazards from fire and preventive measures for HMOs is contained in the Housing Health and Safety Rating System Operating Guidance issued in February 2006 (ISBN: 978 185112 846 4).

The Workplace (Health, Safety and Welfare) Regulations 1992

The Workplace (Health, Safety and Welfare) Regulations 1992 contain some requirements which affect building design. The main requirements are now covered by the Building Regulations but for further information see: *Workplace health, safety and welfare, The Workplace (Health, Safety and Welfare) Regulations 1992, Approved Code of Practice and Guidance;* The Health and Safety Commission, L24; published by HMSO 1992; ISBN: 0 11886 333 9.

The Workplace (Health, Safety and Welfare) Regulations 1992 apply to the common parts of flats and similar buildings if people such as cleaners, wardens and caretakers are employed to work in these common parts. Where the requirements of the Building Regulations that are covered by this Part do not apply to dwellings, the provisions may still be required in the situations described above in order to satisfy the Workplace Regulations.

The Construction (Design and Management) Regulations 2006

The purpose of this Approved Document is to provide guidance on the fire safety requirements for the completed building. It does not address the risk of fire during the construction work which is covered by the Construction (Design and Management) Regulations 2006 and the Regulatory Reform (Fire Safety) Order. HSE has issued the following guidance on fire safety in construction: Construction Information Sheet No 51 *Construction fire safety*; and HSG 168 *Fire safety in construction work* (ISBN: 0 71761 332 1).

When the construction work is being carried out on a building which, apart from the construction site part of the building, is occupied, the Fire and Rescue Authority is responsible for the enforcement of the 2006 Regulations in respect of fire. Where the building is unoccupied, the Health and Safety Executive is responsible for enforcement on the construction site.

Environmental Protection

Requirements under Part B of the Building Regulations and the guidance in this Approved Document are made for the purpose of ensuring the health and safety of people in and around buildings.

The Environment Agency publishes guidance on the design and construction of buildings for the purpose of protecting the environment. This includes Pollution Prevention Guidelines (PPG18) on *Managing Fire Water and Major Spillages,* which seeks to minimise the effects of water run-off from firefighting. It is aimed at medium to large (and small, high-risk) commercial and industrial sites and sets out requirements for the construction of containment areas for contaminated water and such other measures.

It should be noted that compliance with the Building Regulations does not depend upon compliance with other such guidance.

General introduction: Fire safety

Scope

0.1 Approved Document B (Fire safety) has been published in two volumes. Volume 1 deals solely with dwellinghouses (see Appendix E and Building Regulation 2(1)), while Volume 2 deals with all other types of building covered by the Building Regulations.

Where very large (over 18m in height) or unusual dwellinghouses are proposed some of the guidance in Volume 2 may be needed to supplement that given by Volume 1.

Arrangement of sections

0.2 The functional requirements B1 to B5 of Schedule 1 of the Building Regulations are dealt with separately in one or more Sections. The requirement is reproduced at the start of the relevant Sections, followed by an introduction to the subject.

0.3 The provisions set out in this document deal with different aspects of fire safety, with the following aims:

B1: To ensure satisfactory provision of means of giving an alarm of fire and a satisfactory standard of means of escape for persons in the event of fire in a building.

B2: To ensure fire spread over the internal linings of buildings is inhibited.

B3: To ensure the stability of buildings in the event of fire; to ensure that there is a sufficient degree of fire separation within buildings and between adjoining buildings; to provide automatic fire suppression where necessary; and to inhibit the unseen spread of fire and smoke in concealed spaces in buildings.

B4: To ensure external walls and roofs have adequate resistance to the spread of fire over the external envelope, and that spread of fire from one building to another is restricted.

B5: To ensure satisfactory access for fire appliances to buildings and the provision of facilities in buildings to assist firefighters in the saving of life of people in and around buildings.

0.4 Whilst guidance appropriate to each of these aspects is set out separately in this document, many of the provisions are closely interlinked. For example, there is a close link between the provisions for means of escape (B1) and those for the control of fire growth (B2), fire containment and/or suppression (B3) and facilities for the fire and rescue service (B5). Similarly there are links between B3 and the provisions for controlling external fire spread (B4), and between B3 and B5. Interaction between these different requirements should be recognised where variations in the standard of provision are being considered. A higher standard under one of the requirements may be of benefit in respect of one or more of the other requirements. The guidance in the document as a whole should be considered as a package aimed at achieving an acceptable standard of fire safety.

Appendices: provisions common to more than one of Part B's requirements

0.5 Guidance on matters that refer to more than one of the Sections is in a series of Appendices, covering the following subjects:

Appendix A – fire performance of materials, products and structures

Appendix B – provisions regarding fire doors

Appendix C – methods of measurement

Appendix D – a classification of purpose groups

Appendix E – definitions

Appendix F – Standards and other publications referred to.

Fire performance of materials, products and structures

0.6 Much of the guidance throughout this document is given in terms of performance in relation to standard fire test methods. Details are drawn together in Appendix A to which reference is made where appropriate. In the case of fire protection systems, reference is made to standards for system design and installation. Standards referred to are listed in Appendix F.

Fire doors

0.7 Guidance in respect of fire doors is set out in Appendix B.

Methods of measurement

0.8 Some form of measurement is an integral part of much of the guidance in this document and methods are set out in Appendix C.

Purpose groups

0.9 Much of the guidance in this document is related to the use of the building. The use classifications are termed purpose groups, and they are described in Appendix D. This document deals only with buildings in Purpose Groups 1b and 1c.

Definitions

0.10 The definitions are given in Appendix E.

Building maintenance and the provision of information

0.11 For the provisions of this Approved Document to be effective it is essential that the measures incorporated into the design of a dwellinghouse are adequately maintained. Building Regulations do not impose any requirements on the management of a building. However, the eventual owners and occupiers should be provided with sufficient information to operate, maintain and use the building in reasonable safety.

For individual dwellinghouses, basic advice on the proper use and maintenance of systems provided in the building, such as emergency egress windows, fire doors, smoke alarms, sprinklers etc., can help to ensure that these systems are maintained and kept available for use. Householders should also be made aware that unauthorised material alterations (see paragraph 0.20) may leave them liable to prosecution.

In providing fire protection of any kind in dwellinghouses, it should be recognised that measures which significantly interfere with the day-to-day convenience of the occupants may be less reliable in the long term.

Property protection

0.12 There are often many stakeholders, including insurers, who have a valid interest in the fire protection measures which are incorporated into a building's design. To ensure that the most effective fire protection measures are applied which are appropriate to the specific property, early consultation with the main stakeholders is essential. Failure to consult with stakeholders at an early stage could result in additional measures being required after completion, the use of the building being restricted, or insurance premiums and/or deductibles being increased.

Building Regulations are intended to ensure that a reasonable standard of life safety is provided in case of fire. The protection of property, including the building itself, often requires additional measures and insurers will, in general, seek their own higher standards before accepting the insurance risk.

Guidance for asset protection in the Civil and Defence Estates is given in the *Crown Fire Standards* published by the Property Advisers to the Civil Estate (PACE).

Independent schemes of certification and accreditation

0.13 Much of the guidance throughout this document is given in terms of performance in relation to standard fire test methods. Details are drawn together in Appendix A to which reference is made where appropriate. In the case of fire protection systems, reference is made to standards for system design and installation. Standards referred to are listed in Appendix F.

0.14 Since the performance of a system, product, component or structure is dependent

upon satisfactory site installation, testing and maintenance, independent schemes of certification and accreditation of installers and maintenance firms of such will provide confidence in the appropriate standard of workmanship being provided.

Confidence that the required level of performance can be achieved will be demonstrated by the use of a system, material, product or structure which is provided under the arrangements of a product conformity certification scheme and an accreditation of installers scheme.

Third party accredited product conformity certification schemes not only provide a means of identifying materials and designs of systems, products or structures which have demonstrated that they have the requisite performance in fire, but additionally provide confidence that the systems, materials, products or structures actually supplied are provided to the same specification or design as that tested/assessed.

Third party accreditation of installers of systems, materials, products or structures provides a means of ensuring that installations have been conducted by knowledgeable contractors to appropriate standards, thereby increasing the reliability of the anticipated performance in fire.

Many certification bodies which approve such schemes are accredited by UKAS.

0.15 Building Control Bodies may accept the certification of products, components, materials or structures under such schemes as evidence of compliance with the relevant standard. Similarly, Building Control Bodies may accept the certification of the installation or maintenance of products, components, materials or structures under such schemes as evidence of compliance with the relevant standard. Nonetheless, a Building Control Body will wish to establish, in advance of the work, that any such scheme is adequate for the purposes of the Building Regulations.

Residential sprinklers

0.16 Sprinkler systems installed in dwellinghouses can reduce the risk to life and significantly reduce the degree of damage caused by fire. Sprinkler protection can also sometimes be used as a compensatory feature where the provisions of this Approved Document are varied in some way.

0.17 Where a sprinkler system is recommended within this document it should be designed and installed in accordance with BS 9251:2005 *Sprinkler systems for residential and domestic occupancies – Code of practice* and DD 252:2002 *Components for residential sprinkler systems – Specification and test methods for residential sprinklers.*

Where sprinklers are provided, it is normal practice to provide sprinkler protection throughout the building. However, where the sprinklers are being installed as a compensatory feature to address a specific risk or hazard it may be acceptable to protect only part of a building.

Further guidance can also be found in *Sprinklers for Safety: Use and Benefits of Incorporating Sprinklers in Buildings and Structures*, BAFSA (2006) ISBN: 0 95526 280 1.

0.18 There are many alternative or innovative fire suppression systems available. Where these are used it is necessary to ensure that such systems have been designed and tested for use in domestic buildings and are fit for their intended purpose.

Inclusive design

0.19 The fire safety aspects of the Building Regulations are made for securing reasonable standards of health and safety of persons in and about buildings. This is intended to include all people including people with disabilities. The provisions set out in this Approved Document are considered to be a reasonable standard for most buildings. However, there may be some people whose specific needs are not addressed. In some situations additional measures may be needed to accommodate these needs. This should be done on a case by case basis.

Material alteration

0.20 Under Regulation 3, the term "material alteration" is defined by reference to a list of "relevant requirements" of Schedule 1 to the Building Regulations. That list includes the requirements of Parts B1, B3, B4 and B5. This means that an alteration which, at any stage of the work, results in a building being less satisfactory than it was before in relation to compliance with the requirements of Parts B1, B3, B4 or B5 is a material alteration, and is therefore controlled by Regulation 4 as it is classed as "building work". Regulation 4(1) requires that any building work carried out in relation to a material alteration complies with the applicable requirements of Schedule 1 to the Regulations, while Regulation 4(3) requires that once that building work has been completed, the building as a whole must comply with the relevant requirements of Schedule 1 or, where it did not comply before, must be no more unsatisfactory than it was before the work was carried out.

Alternative approaches

0.21 The fire safety requirements of the Building Regulations should be satisfied by following the relevant guidance given in this Approved Document. However, Approved Documents are intended to provide guidance for some of the more common building situations and there may well be alternative ways of achieving compliance with the requirements.

If other codes or guides are adopted, the relevant recommendations concerning fire safety in the particular publication should be followed, rather than a mixture of the publication and provisions in the relevant sections of this Approved Document. However, there may be circumstances where it is necessary to use one publication to supplement another.

Guidance documents intended specifically for assessing fire safety in **existing buildings** will often include provisions which are less onerous than those set out in this Approved Document or other standards applicable to new buildings. As such, these documents are unlikely to be appropriate for use where building work, controlled by the Regulations, is proposed.

Registered group homes

0.22 Depending on the nature of the occupants and their management needs, it may be acceptable to treat an unsupervised group home with up to six residents as an ordinary dwellinghouse. However, because such places have to be registered, the registration authority should be consulted to establish whether there are any additional fire safety measures that the authority will require.

Where an existing house of one or two storeys is to be put to use as an unsupervised group home for not more than 6 mental health service users, it should be regarded as a Purpose Group 1(c) building if the means of escape are provided in accordance with HTM 88: *Guide to fire precautions in NHS housing in the community for mentally handicapped (or mentally ill) people*. Where the building is new, it may be more appropriate to regard it as being in Purpose Group 2(b).

Adult placements

0.23 Where a dwellinghouse is used for the purposes of an Adult Placement Scheme and fulfils the criteria of the Adult Placement Schemes (England) Regulations (SI 2004 No 2070) and where no building work is proposed, the guidance in the joint code of practice published by the National Association of Adult Placement Services (www.naaps.co.uk) should be sufficient to satisfy Part B of the Building Regulations if a material change of use has taken place.

Sheltered housing

0.24 Where a sheltered housing scheme consists of individual houses then each unit may be designed in accordance with this volume of Approved Document B. Any communal facilities that are provided within the scheme should be designed in accordance with Approved Document B Volume 2 (Buildings other than dwellinghouses).

Fire safety engineering

0.25 Fire safety engineering can provide an alternative approach to fire safety. It may be the only practical way to achieve a satisfactory standard of fire safety in some large and complex buildings. Fire safety engineering may also be suitable for solving a problem with an aspect of the building design which otherwise follows the provisions in this document.

British Standard BS 7974:2001 *Application of fire safety engineering principles to the design of buildings* and supporting published documents (PDs) provide a framework and guidance on the design and assessment of fire safety measures in buildings. Following the discipline of BS 7974 should enable designers and Building Control Bodies to be aware of the relevant issues, the need to consider the complete fire safety system, and to follow a disciplined analytical framework.

0.26 Factors that should be taken into account include:

a. the anticipated probability of a fire occurring;

b. the anticipated fire severity;

c. the ability of a structure to resist the spread of fire and smoke; and

d. the consequential danger to people in and around the building.

0.27 A wide variety of measures could be considered and incorporated to a greater or lesser extent, as appropriate in the circumstances. These include:

a. the adequacy of means to prevent fire;

b. early fire warning by an automatic detection and warning system;

c. the standard of means of escape;

d. provision of smoke control;

e. control of the rate of growth of a fire;

f. the adequacy of the structure to resist the effects of a fire;

g. the degree of fire containment;

h. fire separation between buildings or parts of buildings;

i. the standard of active measures for fire extinguishment or control;

j. facilities to assist the fire and rescue service;

k. the availability of powers to require staff training in fire safety and fire routines;

l. consideration of the availability of any continuing control under other legislation that could ensure continued maintenance of such systems; and

m. management.

0.28 It is possible to use quantitative techniques to evaluate risk and hazard. Some factors in the measures listed above can be given numerical values in some circumstances. The assumptions made when quantitative methods are used need careful assessment.

Buildings of special architectural or historic interest

0.29 Some variation of the provisions set out in this document may also be appropriate where Part B applies to existing buildings, particularly in buildings of special architectural or historic interest, where adherence to the guidance in this document might prove unduly restrictive. In such cases it would be appropriate to take into account a range of fire safety features, some of which are dealt with in this document, and some of which are not addressed in any detail, and to set these against an assessment of the hazard and risk peculiar to the particular case.

The Requirement

This Approved Document deals with the following Requirement from Part B of Schedule 1 to the Building Regulations 2010.

Requirement	Limits on application
Means of warning and escape **B1.** The building shall be designed and constructed so that there are appropriate provisions for the early warning of fire, and appropriate means of escape in case of fire from the building to a place of safety outside the building capable of being safely and effectively used at all material times. (a) 1952 C.52; Section 33 was amended by Section 100 of the Criminal Justice and Public Order Act 1994 (C.33) and by S.I. 1963/597.	Requirement B1 does not apply to any prison provided under Section 33 of the Prison Act 1952(a) (power to provide prisons, etc.).

Guidance

Performance

In the Secretary of State's view the Requirement B1 will be met if:

a. there is sufficient means for giving early warning of fire for persons in the building;

b. there are routes of sufficient number and capacity, which are suitably located to enable persons to escape to a place of safety in the event of fire; and

c. the routes are sufficiently protected from the effects of fire, where necessary.

Introduction

B1.i These provisions relate to building work and material changes of use which are subject to the functional requirement B1; they may therefore affect new or existing buildings. They are concerned with the measures necessary to ensure reasonable facilities for means of warning and escape in case of fire. They are only concerned with fire precautions where these are necessary to safeguard escape routes.

They assume that in the design of the building, reliance should not be placed on external rescue by the fire and rescue service nor should it be based on a presumption that they will attend an incident within a given time. This Approved Document has been prepared on the basis that, in an emergency, the occupants of any part of a building should be able to escape safely without any external assistance.

It should also be noted that the guidance for a typical one or two storey dwellinghouse is limited to the provision of smoke alarms and to the provision of openable windows for emergency egress.

Analysis of the problem

B1.ii The design of means of escape and the provision of other fire safety measures, such as smoke alarms, should be based on an assessment of the risk to the occupants in the event of fire. The assessment should take into account the nature of the building structure; the use of the building; the potential of fire spread through the building; and the standard of fire safety management proposed. Where it is not possible to identify with any certainty any of these elements, a judgement as to the likely level of provision must be made.

B1.iii Fires do not normally start in two different places in a building at the same time. Initially, a fire will create a hazard only in the part in which it starts and it is unlikely, at this stage, to involve a large area. The fire may subsequently spread to other parts of the building, usually along the circulation routes. The items that are the first to be ignited are often furnishings and other items

not controlled by the Building Regulations. It is less likely that the fire will originate in the structure of the building itself and the risk of it originating accidentally in circulation areas is limited, provided that the combustible content of such areas is restricted.

B1.iv The primary danger associated with fire in its early stages is not flame but the smoke and noxious gases produced by the fire. They cause most of the casualties and may also obscure the way to escape routes and exits. Measures designed to provide safe means of escape must therefore provide appropriate arrangements to limit the rapid spread of smoke and fumes.

Criteria for means of escape

B1.v The basic principles for the design of means of escape are:

a. that there should be alternative means of escape from most situations;

b. where direct escape to a place of safety is not possible, it should be possible to reach a place of relative safety, such as a protected stairway, which is on a route to an exit, within a reasonable travel distance; and

c. in certain conditions, a single direction of escape (a dead end) can be accepted as providing reasonable safety. These conditions depend on the use of the building and its associated fire risk, the size and height of the building, the extent of the dead end and the numbers of persons accommodated within the dead end.

The ultimate place of safety is the open air clear of the effects of the fire.

B1.vi For the purposes of Building Regulations, the following are not acceptable as means of escape:

a. lifts (except for a suitably designed and installed evacuation lift);

b. portable ladders and throw-out ladders; and

c. manipulative apparatus and appliances, e.g. fold-down ladders and chutes.

Note: The regulations would not prohibit the use of such measures as an additional feature but they are not considered suitable as an alternative to adequate means of escape.

Unprotected and protected escape routes

B1.vii The unprotected part of an escape route is that part which a person has to traverse before reaching either the safety of a final exit or the comparative safety of a protected escape route, i.e. a protected corridor or protected stairway.

Unprotected escape routes should be limited in extent so that people do not have to travel excessive distances while exposed to the immediate danger of fire and smoke.

Even with protected horizontal escape routes the distance to a final exit or protected stairway needs to be limited because the structure does not give protection indefinitely.

B1.viii Protected stairways are designed to provide virtually 'fire sterile' areas which lead to places of safety outside the building. Once inside a protected stairway, a person can be considered to be safe from immediate danger from flame and smoke. They can then proceed to a place of safety at their own pace. To enable this to be done, flames, smoke and gases must be excluded from these escape routes, as far as is reasonably possible, by fire-resisting construction and doors or by an appropriate smoke control system, or by a combination of both of these methods.

Security

B1.ix The need for easy and rapid evacuation of a building in case of fire may conflict with the control of entry and exit in the interest of security. Measures intended to prevent unauthorised access can also hinder entry of the fire and rescue service to rescue people trapped by fire.

Potential conflicts should be identified and resolved at the design stage and not left until after completion of the work. The architectural liaison officers attached to most police forces are a valuable source of advice.

This document does not intend for the types of lock used on windows (see paragraph 2.8) and entrance doors to dwellinghouses to be controlled under the Building Regulations.

General

Use of the document

B1.x Section 1 deals with fire detection and alarm systems. Section 2 deals with means of escape.

Section 1: Fire detection and fire alarm systems

Introduction

1.1 Provisions are made in this section for suitable arrangements to be made in dwellinghouses to give early warning in the event of fire.

General

1.2 The installation of smoke alarms, or automatic fire detection and alarm systems can significantly increase the level of safety by automatically giving an early warning of fire. The following guidance is appropriate for most dwellinghouses. However, where it is known that the occupants of a proposed dwellinghouse are at a special risk from fire, it may be more appropriate to provide a higher standard of protection, e.g. additional detectors.

1.3 All new dwellinghouses should be provided with a fire detection and fire alarm system in accordance with the relevant recommendations of BS 5839-6:2004 to at least a Grade D Category LD3 standard.

1.4 The smoke and heat alarms should be mains-operated and conform to BS EN 14604: 2005, Smoke alarm devices or BS 5446-2:2003, Fire detection and fire alarm devices for dwellinghouses, Part 2 Specification for heat alarms, respectively. They should have a standby power supply, such as a battery (either rechargeable or non-rechargeable) or capacitor. More information on power supplies is given in clause 15 of BS 5839-6:2004.

Note: BS EN 14604 covers smoke alarms based on ionization chamber smoke detectors and optical (photo-electric) smoke detectors. The different types of detector respond differently to smouldering and fast-flaming fires. Either type of detector is generally suitable. However, the choice of detector type should, if possible, take into account the type of fire that might be expected and the need to avoid false alarms. Optical detectors tend to be less affected by low levels of 'invisible' particles, such as fumes from kitchens, that often cause false alarms. Accordingly, they are generally more suitable than ionization chamber detectors for installation in circulation spaces adjacent to kitchens.

Large houses

1.5 A dwellinghouse is regarded as large if it has more than one storey and any of those storeys exceed 200m^2.

1.6 A large dwellinghouse of 2 storeys (excluding basement storeys) should be fitted with a fire detection and fire alarm system of Grade B category LD3 as described in BS 5839-6:2004.

1.7 A large dwellinghouse of 3 or more storeys (excluding basement storeys) should be fitted with a Grade A Category LD2 system as described in BS 5839-6:2004, with detectors sited in accordance with the recommendations of BS 5839-1:2002 for a Category L2 system.

Material alterations

1.8 Where new habitable rooms are provided above the ground floor level, or where they are provided at ground floor level and there is no final exit from the new room, a fire detection and fire alarm system should be installed. Smoke alarms should be provided in the circulation spaces of the dwellinghouse in accordance with paragraphs 1.10 to 1.18 to ensure that any occupants of the new rooms are warned of any fire that may impede their escape.

Sheltered housing

1.9 The detection equipment in a sheltered housing scheme with a warden or supervisor should have a connection to a central monitoring point (or alarm receiving centre) so that the person in charge is aware that a fire has been detected in one of the dwellinghouses and can identify the dwellinghouse concerned. These provisions are not intended to be applied to the common parts of a sheltered housing development, such as communal lounges, or to sheltered accommodation in the Institutional or Other residential purpose groups (see Approved Document B Volume 2).

Positioning of smoke and heat alarms

1.10 Detailed guidance on the design and installation of fire detection and alarm systems in dwellinghouses is given in BS 5839-6:2004. However, the following guidance is appropriate to most common situations.

1.11 Smoke alarms should normally be positioned in the circulation spaces between sleeping spaces and places where fires are most likely to start (e.g. kitchens and living rooms) to pick up smoke in the early stages of a fire.

1.12 There should be at least one smoke alarm on every storey of a dwellinghouse.

1.13 Where the kitchen area is not separated from the stairway or circulation space by a door, there should be a compatible interlinked heat detector or heat alarm in the kitchen, in addition to whatever smoke alarms are needed in the circulation space(s).

1.14   Where more than one alarm is installed they should be linked so that the detection of smoke or heat by one unit operates the alarm signal in all of them. The manufacturers' instructions about the maximum number of units that can be linked should be observed.

1.15   Smoke alarms/detectors should be sited so that:

a.   there is a smoke alarm in the circulation space within 7.5m of the door to every habitable room;

b.   they are ceiling-mounted and at least 300mm from walls and light fittings (unless, in the case of light fittings, there is test evidence to prove that the proximity of the light fitting will not adversely affect the efficiency of the detector). Units designed for wall-mounting may also be used provided that the units are above the level of doorways opening into the space and they are fixed in accordance with manufacturers' instructions; and

c.   the sensor in ceiling-mounted devices is between 25mm and 600mm below the ceiling (25-150mm in the case of heat detectors or heat alarms).

Note: This guidance applies to ceilings that are predominantly flat and horizontal.

1.16   It should be possible to reach the smoke alarms to carry out routine maintenance, such as testing and cleaning, easily and safely. For this reason smoke alarms should not be fixed over a stair or any other opening between floors.

1.17   Smoke alarms should not be fixed next to or directly above heaters or air-conditioning outlets. They should not be fixed in bathrooms, showers, cooking areas or garages, or any other place where steam, condensation or fumes could give false alarms.

1.18   Smoke alarms should not be fitted in places that get very hot (such as a boiler room) or very cold (such as an unheated porch). They should not be fixed to surfaces which are normally much warmer or colder than the rest of the space, because the temperature difference might create air currents which move smoke away from the unit.

Power supplies

1.19   The power supply for a smoke alarm system should be derived from the dwellinghouse's mains electricity supply. The mains supply to the smoke alarm(s) should comprise a single independent circuit at the dwellinghouse's main distribution board (consumer unit) or a single regularly used local lighting circuit. This has the advantage that the circuit is unlikely to be disconnected for any prolonged period. There should be a means of isolating power to the smoke alarms without isolating the lighting.

1.20   The electrical installation should comply with Approved Document P (Electrical safety).

1.21   Any cable suitable for domestic wiring may be used for the power supply and interconnection to smoke alarm systems. It does not need any particular fire survival properties except in large houses (BS 5839-6:2004 specifies fire resisting cables for Grade A and B systems). Any conductors used for interconnecting alarms (signalling) should be readily distinguishable from those supplying mains power, e.g. by colour coding.

Note: Mains-powered smoke alarms may be interconnected using radio-links, provided that this does not reduce the lifetime or duration of any standby power supply below 72 hours. In this case, the smoke alarms may be connected to separate power circuits (see paragraph 1.19)

1.22   Other effective options exist and are described in BS 5839-1:2002 and BS 5839-6:2004. For example, the mains supply may be reduced to extra low voltage in a control unit incorporating a standby trickle-charged battery, before being distributed at that voltage to the alarms.

Design and installation of systems

1.23   It is essential that fire detection and fire alarm systems are properly designed, installed and maintained. Where a fire alarm system is installed, an installation and commissioning certificate should be provided. Third party certification schemes for fire protection products and related services are an effective means of providing the fullest possible assurances, offering a level of quality, reliability and safety.

1.24   A requirement for maintenance cannot be made as a condition of passing plans by the Building Control Body. However, the attention of developers and builders is drawn to the importance of providing the occupants with information on the use of the equipment, and on its maintenance (or guidance on suitable maintenance contractors). See paragraph 0.11.

Note: BS 5839-1 and BS 5839-6 recommend that occupiers should receive the manufacturers' instructions concerning the operation and maintenance of the alarm system.

Section 2: Means of escape

Introduction

2.1 The means of escape from a typical one or two storey dwellinghouse is relatively simple to provide. Few provisions are specified in this document beyond ensuring that means are provided for giving early warning in the event of fire (see Section 1) and that suitable means are provided for emergency egress from each storey via windows or doors.

With increasing height more complex provisions are needed because emergency egress through upper windows becomes increasingly hazardous. It is then necessary to protect the internal stairway. If there are floors more than 7.5m above ground level, the risk that the stairway will become impassable before occupants of the upper parts of the dwellinghouse have escaped is appreciable, and an alternative route from those parts should be provided. See Diagram 1.

Note: Ground level is explained in Appendix C, Diagram C1.

2.2 In providing any kind of fire protection in houses it should be recognised that measures which significantly interfere with the day-to-day convenience of the occupants may be less reliable in the long term.

Provisions for escape from the ground storey

2.3 Except for kitchens, all habitable rooms in the ground storey should either:

a. open directly onto a hall leading to the entrance or other suitable exit; or

b. be provided with a window (or door) which complies with paragraph 2.8.

Note: See also General Provisions.

Provisions for escape from upper floors not more than 4.5m above ground level

2.4 Except for kitchens, all habitable rooms in the upper storey(s) of a dwellinghouse served by only one stair should be provided with:

a. a window (or external door) which complies with paragraph 2.8; or

b. direct access to a protected stairway (as described in 2.6 (a) or (b)).

Note: A single window can be accepted to serve two rooms provided both rooms have their own access to the stairs. A communicating door between the rooms should also be provided so that it is possible to gain access to the window without passing through the stair enclosure.

Note: See also General Provisions.

Provisions for escape from upper floors more than 4.5m above ground level

2.5 The provisions described in 2.6 and 2.7 need not be followed if the dwellinghouse has more than one internal stairway, which afford effective alternative means of escape and are physically separated from each other.

Note: The necessary degree of separation is a matter of judgement, eg. stairs may be separated by fire-resisting construction or by a number of rooms.

Dwellinghouses with one floor more than 4.5m above ground level

2.6 The dwellinghouse may either have a protected stairway as described in (a) below, or the top floor can be separated and given its own alternative escape route as described in (b).

a. The upper storeys (those above ground storey) should be served by a protected stairway (protected at all levels) which should either:

    i. extend to a final exit, see Diagram 2(a); or

    ii. give access to at least two escape routes at ground level, each delivering to final exits and separated from each other by fire-resisting construction and fire doors, see Diagram 2(b); or

b. The top storey should be separated from the lower storeys by fire-resisting construction and be provided with an alternative escape route leading to its own final exit. See Diagram 3.

Note: See also General Provisions.

Dwellinghouses with more than one floor over 4.5m above ground level

2.7 Where a dwellinghouse has two or more storeys with floors more than 4.5m above ground level (typically a dwellinghouse of four or more storeys) then, in addition to meeting the provisions in paragraph 2.6:

a. an alternative escape route should be provided from each storey or level situated 7.5m or more above ground level. Where the access to the alternative escape route is via:

    i. the protected stairway to an upper storey; or

    ii. a landing within the protected stairway enclosure to an alternative escape route on the same storey; then

    iii. the protected stairway at or about 7.5m above ground level should be separated from the lower storeys or levels by fire-resisting construction, see Diagram 3; or

b. the dwellinghouse should be fitted throughout with a sprinkler system designed and installed in accordance with BS 9251:2005.

Note: See also General Provisions.

Diagram 1   **Means of escape from dwellinghouses**

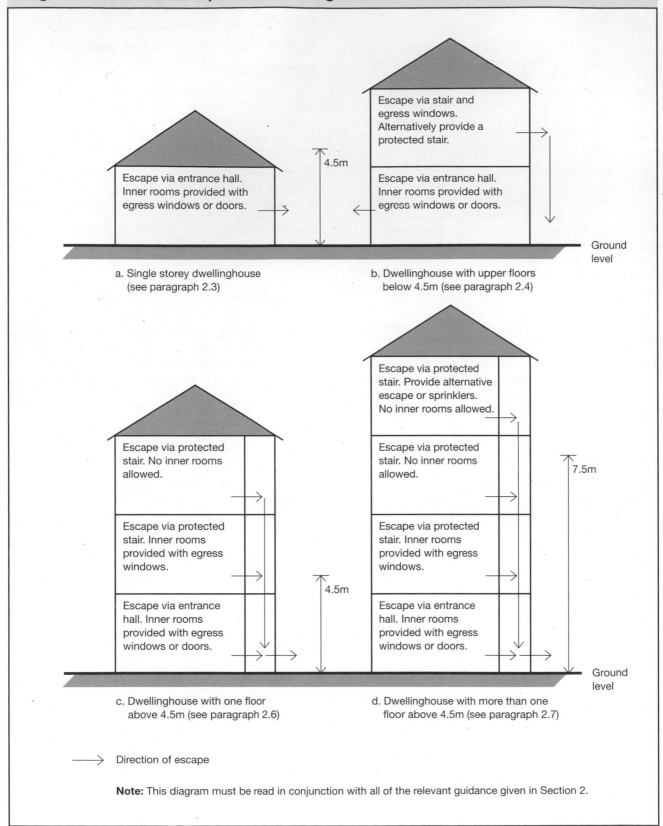

4.5m

Escape via entrance hall.
Inner rooms provided with
egress windows or doors.

a. Single storey dwellinghouse
  (see paragraph 2.3)

Escape via stair and
egress windows.
Alternatively provide a
protected stair.

Escape via entrance hall.
Inner rooms provided with
egress windows or doors.

b. Dwellinghouse with upper floors
  below 4.5m (see paragraph 2.4)

Escape via protected
stair. No inner rooms
allowed.

Escape via protected
stair. Inner rooms
provided with egress
windows.

Escape via entrance
hall. Inner rooms
provided with egress
windows or doors.

4.5m

c. Dwellinghouse with one floor
  above 4.5m (see paragraph 2.6)

Escape via protected
stair. Provide alternative
escape or sprinklers.
No inner rooms allowed.

Escape via protected
stair. No inner rooms
allowed.

Escape via protected
stair. Inner rooms
provided with egress
windows.

Escape via entrance
hall. Inner rooms
provided with egress
windows or doors.

7.5m

d. Dwellinghouse with more than one
  floor above 4.5m (see paragraph 2.7)

Ground
level

⟶   Direction of escape

Note: This diagram must be read in conjunction with all of the relevant guidance given in Section 2.

Diagram 2 Alternative arrangements for final exits

See para 2.6(a)

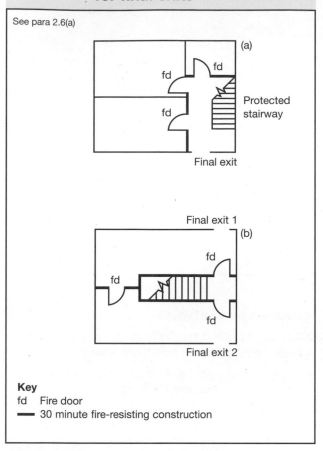

Diagram 3 Fire separation in houses with more than one floor over 4.5m above ground level

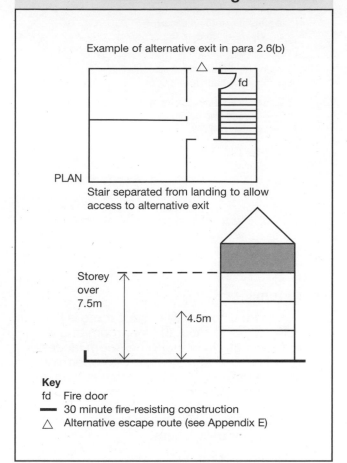

General provisions

Emergency egress windows and external doors

2.8 Any window provided for emergency egress purposes and any external door provided for escape should comply with the following conditions:

a. the window should have an unobstructed openable area that is at least 0.33m² and at least 450mm high and 450mm wide (the route through the window may be at an angle rather than straight through). The bottom of the openable area should be not more than 1100mm above the floor; and

b. the window or door should enable the person escaping to reach a place free from danger from fire. This is a matter for judgement in each case, but, in general, a courtyard or back garden from which there is no exit other than through other buildings would have to be at least as deep as the dwellinghouse is high to be acceptable, see Diagram 4.

Note 1: Approved Document K *Protection from falling, collision and impact* specifies a minimum guarding height of 800mm, except in the case of a window in a roof where the bottom of the opening may be 600mm above the floor.

Note 2: Locks (with or without removable keys) and stays may be fitted to egress windows, subject to the stay being fitted with a release catch, which may be child resistant.

Note 3: Windows should be designed such that they will remain in the open position without needing to be held by a person making their escape.

Diagram 4 Ground or basement storey exit into an enclosed space

See para 2.8(b)

For an escape route to be acceptable into an enclosed courtyard or garden, the depth of back garden should exceed:

a. the height of the house above ground level (X); or

b. where a rear extension is provided, the height of the extensions (Y)

whichever is greater.

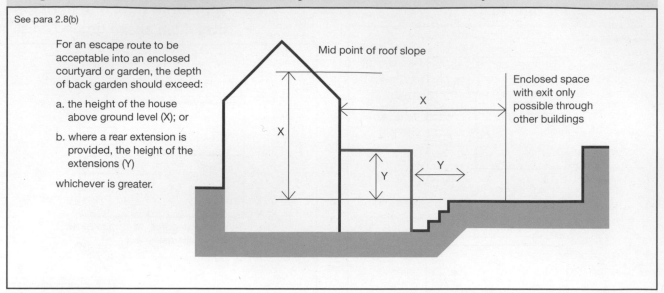

Mid point of roof slope

Enclosed space with exit only possible through other buildings

Inner rooms

2.9   A room whose only escape route is through another room is termed an inner room and is at risk if a fire starts in that other room (access room). This situation may arise with open-plan layouts and galleries. Such an arrangement is only acceptable where the inner room is:

a. a kitchen;

b. a laundry or utility room;

c. a dressing room;

d. a bathroom, WC, or shower room;

e. any other room on a floor, not more than 4.5m above ground level, provided with an emergency egress window which complies with paragraph 2.8; or

f. a gallery which complies with paragraph 2.12.

Note: A room accessed only via an inner room (an inner-inner room) may be acceptable if it complies with the above, not more than one door separates the room from an interlinked smoke alarm and none of the access rooms is a kitchen.

Balconies and flat roofs

2.10   A flat roof forming part of a means of escape should comply with the following provisions:

a. the roof should be part of the same building from which escape is being made;

b. the route across the roof should lead to a storey exit or external escape route; and

c. the part of the roof forming the escape route and its supporting structure, together with any opening within 3m of the escape route, should provide 30 minutes fire resistance (see Appendix A, Table A1).

2.11   Where a balcony or flat roof is provided for escape purposes guarding may be needed, in which case it should meet the provisions in Approved Document K *Protection from falling, collision and impact.*

Galleries

2.12 A gallery should be provided with an alternative exit or, where the gallery floor is not more than 4.5m above ground level, an emergency egress window which complies with paragraph 2.8. Alternatively, where the gallery floor is not provided with an alternative exit or escape window, it should comply with the following;

a. the gallery should overlook at least 50% of the room below (see Diagram 5);

b. the distance between the foot of the access stair to the gallery and the door to the room containing the gallery should not exceed 3m;

c. the distance from the head of the access stair to any point on the gallery should not exceed 7.5m; and

d. any cooking facilities within a room containing a gallery should either:

  i. be enclosed with fire-resisting construction; or

  ii. be remote from the stair to the gallery and positioned such that they do not prejudice the escape from the gallery.

Basements

2.13 Because of the risk that a single stairway may be blocked by smoke from a fire in the basement or ground storey, if the basement storey contains any habitable room, the dwellinghouse should be provided with either:

a. an external door or window suitable for egress from the basement (see paragraph 2.8); or

b. a protected stairway leading from the basement to a final exit.

Cavity barriers

2.14 Cavity barriers should be provided above the enclosures to a protected stairway in a dwellinghouse with a floor more than 4.5m above ground level (see Diagram 6).

Diagram 5 **Gallery floors with no alternative exit**

See para 2.12

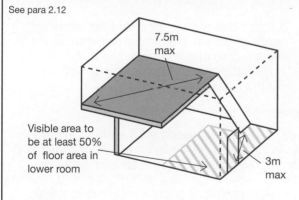

7.5m max

Visible area to be at least 50% of floor area in lower room

3m max

Notes:

1 This diagram does not apply where the gallery is
  i. provided with an alternative escape route; or
  ii. provided with an emergency egress window (where the gallery floor is not more than 4.5m above ground level).

2 Any cooking facilities within a room containing a gallery should either:
  i. be enclosed with fire-resisting construction; or
  ii. be remote from the stair to the gallery and positioned such that they do not prejudice the escape from the gallery.

Diagram 6 **Alternative cavity barrier arrangements in roof space over protected stairway in a house with a floor more than 4.5m above ground level**

See para 2.14

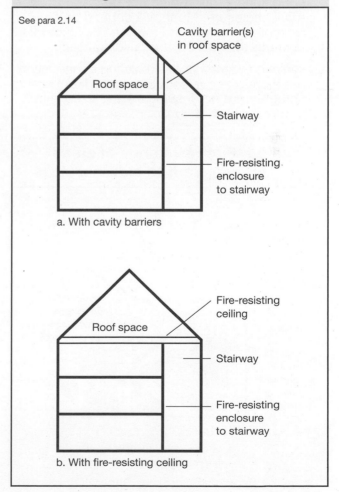

Cavity barrier(s) in roof space

Roof space

Stairway

Fire-resisting enclosure to stairway

a. With cavity barriers

Fire-resisting ceiling

Roof space

Stairway

Fire-resisting enclosure to stairway

b. With fire-resisting ceiling

External escape stairs

2.15   Where an external escape stair is provided, it should meet the following provisions:

a. All doors giving access to the stair should be fire-resisting, except that a fire-resisting door is not required at the head of any stair leading downwards where there is only one exit from the building onto the top landing.

b. Any part of the external envelope of the building within 1800mm of (and 9m vertically below) the flights and landings of an external escape stair should be of fire-resisting construction, except that the 1800mm dimension may be reduced to 1100mm above the top level of the stair if it is not a stair up from a basement to ground level (see Diagram 7).

c. There is protection by fire-resisting construction for any part of the building (including any doors) within 1800mm of the escape route from the stair to a place of safety, unless there is a choice of routes from the foot of the stair that would enable the people escaping to avoid exposure to the effects of the fire in the adjoining building.

d. Any stair more than 6m in vertical extent is protected from the effects of adverse weather conditions. (This should not be taken to imply a full enclosure. Much will depend on the location of the stair and the degree of protection given to the stair by the building itself).

e. Glazing in areas of fire-resisting construction mentioned above should also be fire-resisting (integrity but not insulation) and fixed shut.

Diagram 7   **Fire resistance of areas adjacent to external stairs**

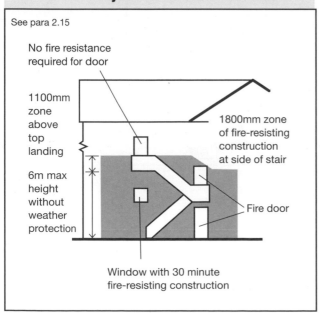

See para 2.15

No fire resistance required for door

1100mm zone above top landing

6m max height without weather protection

1800mm zone of fire-resisting construction at side of stair

Fire door

Window with 30 minute fire-resisting construction

Air circulation systems in houses with a floor more than 4.5m above ground level

2.16   Air circulation systems which circulate air within an individual dwellinghouse with a floor more than 4.5m above ground level should meet the guidance given in paragraph 2.17. Where ventilation ducts pass through compartment walls into another building then the guidance given in Approved Document B Volume 2 should be followed.

2.17   With these types of systems, the following precautions are needed to avoid the possibility of the system allowing smoke or fire to spread into a protected stairway:

a. Transfer grilles should not be fitted in any wall, door, floor or ceiling enclosing a protected stairway.

b. Any duct passing through the enclosure to a protected stairway or entrance hall should be of rigid steel construction and all joints between the ductwork and the enclosure should be fire-stopped.

c. Ventilation ducts supplying or extracting air directly to or from a protected stairway, should not serve other areas as well.

d. Any system of mechanical ventilation which recirculates air and which serves both the stairway and other areas should be designed to shut down on the detection of smoke within the system.

e. A room thermostat for a ducted warm air heating system should be mounted in the living room, at a height between 1370mm and 1830mm, and its maximum setting should not exceed 27°C.

Passenger lifts

2.18   Where a passenger lift is provided in the dwellinghouse and it serves any floor more than 4.5m above ground level, it should either be located in the enclosure to the protected stairway (see paragraph 2.6) or be contained in a fire-resisting lift shaft.

Work on existing houses

Replacement windows

2.19   Regulation 4(1) requires that all "building work", as defined by Regulation 3, complies with the applicable requirements of Schedule 1 to the Building Regulations. The definition of building work in Regulation 3(1) includes the provision or extension of a "controlled service or fitting" in or in connection with a building. The definition of controlled service or fitting is given in Regulation 2(1), and includes a replacement window.

Where windows are to be replaced (but not where they are to be repaired only, as repair work to windows does not fall within the definition of building work) the replacement work should comply with the requirements of Parts L and N of

---

Schedule 1. In addition, the building should not have a lesser level of compliance, after the work has been completed, with other applicable Parts of Schedule 1.

For the purposes of Part B1, where a window is located such that, in a new dwellinghouse, an escape window would be necessary and the window is of sufficient size that it could be used for the purposes of escape then:

a. the replacement window opening should be sized to provide at least the same potential for escape as the window it replaces; or

b. where the original window is larger than necessary for the purposes of escape, the window opening could be reduced down to the minimum specified in paragraph 2.8.

Note: Part B3 makes provisions for cavity barriers around window openings in some forms of construction. Where windows are replaced it may be necessary to consider if adequate protection is maintained.

Material alterations

2.20 Paragraph 0.20 sets out the requirements relating to material alterations. What constitutes reasonable provision where undertaking material alterations would depend on the circumstances in the particular case and would need to take account of historic value (see paragraph 0.29). Possible ways of satisfying the requirements include:

a. Smoke alarms

Where new habitable rooms are provided then smoke alarms should be provided in accordance with paragraph 1.8.

b. Loft conversions

Where a new storey is to be added by converting an existing roof space, the provisions for escape need to be considered throughout the full extent of the escape route. For example, a loft conversion to a two-storey house will result in the need to protect the stairway (by providing fire-resisting doors and partitions) where previously no protection may have existed (see paragraph 2.6a).

Note: If it is considered undesirable to replace existing doors (e.g. if they are of historical or architectural merit) it may be possible to retain the doors or upgrade them to an acceptable standard.

Note: Where an 'open-plan' arrangement exists at ground level it may be necessary to provide a new partition to enclose the escape route (see Diagram 2).

Alternatively, it may be possible to provide sprinkler protection to the open-plan area, in conjunction with a fire-resisting partition and door (E20), in order to separate the ground floor from the upper storeys. This door should be so arranged to allow the occupants of the loft room to access an escape window at first floor level (in accordance with paragraph 2.8) in the event of a fire in the open-plan area. Cooking facilities should be separated from the open-plan area with fire-resisting construction.

The Requirement

This Approved Document deals with the following Requirement from Part B of Schedule 1 to the Building Regulations 2010.

Requirement	Limits on application

Internal fire spread (linings)
 	
B2. (1) To inhibit the spread of fire within the building, the internal linings shall:
 	
    (a) adequately resist the spread of flame over their surfaces; and
 	
    (b) have, if ignited, a rate of heat release or a rate of fire growth, which is reasonable in the circumstances.
 	
    (2) In this paragraph 'internal linings' mean the materials or products used in lining any partition, wall, ceiling or other internal structure.	

Guidance

Performance

In the Secretary of State's view the Requirements of B2 will be met if the spread of flame over the internal linings of the building is restricted by making provision for them to have low rates of surface spread of flame and, in some cases, to have a low rate of heat release, so as to limit the contribution that the fabric of the building makes to fire growth. In relation to the European fire tests and classification system, the requirements of B2 will be met if the heat released from the internal linings is restricted by making provision for them to have a resistance to ignition and a rate of fire growth which are reasonable in the circumstances.

The extent to which this is necessary is dependent on the location of the lining.

Introduction

Fire spread and internal linings

B2.i   The choice of materials for walls and ceilings can significantly affect the spread of a fire and its rate of growth, even though they are not likely to be the materials first ignited.

It is particularly important in circulation spaces where linings may offer the main means by which fire spreads and where rapid spread is most likely to prevent occupants from escaping.

Several properties of lining materials influence fire spread. These include the ease of ignition and the rate at which the lining material gives off heat when burning. The guidance relating to the European fire tests and classification provides for control of internal fire spread through control of these properties. This document does not give detailed guidance on other properties, such as the generation of smoke and fumes.

Floors and stairs

B2.ii   The provisions do not apply to the upper surfaces of floors and stairs because they are not significantly involved in a fire until it is well developed, and thus do not play an important part in fire spread in the early stages of a fire that are most relevant to the safety of occupants.

Other controls on internal surface properties

B2.iii In Section 7 there is guidance on enclosures to above ground drainage system pipes.

Note: External flame spread is dealt with in Sections 8 to 10.

Furniture and fittings

B2.iv Furniture and fittings can have a major effect on fire spread but it is not possible to control them through Building Regulations. They are therefore not dealt with in this Approved Document.

Classification of performance

B2.v   Appendix A describes the different classes of performance and the appropriate methods of test (see paragraphs 7-20).

The national classifications used are based on tests in BS 476 *Fire tests on building materials and structures,* namely BS 476-6:1989 *Method of test for fire propagation for products* and BS 476-7:1997 *Method of test to determine the classification of the surface spread of flame of products.* However, BS 476-4:1970 *Non-combustibility test for materials* and BS 476-11:1982 *Method for assessing the heat emission from building products* are also used as one method of meeting Class 0. Other tests are available for classification of thermoplastic materials if they do not have the appropriate rating under BS 476: Part 7; three ratings, referred to as TP(a) rigid and TP(a) flexible and TP(b), are used.

The European classifications are described in BS EN 13501-1:2002 *Fire classification of construction products and building elements,* Part 1 *Classification using data from reaction to fire tests.* They are based on a combination of four European test methods, namely:

- BS EN ISO 1182:2002, *Reaction to fire tests for building products – Non combustibility test*
- BS EN ISO 1716:2002, *Reaction to fire tests for building products – Determination of the gross calorific value*
- BS EN 13823:2002, *Reaction to fire tests for building products – Building products excluding floorings exposed to the thermal attack by a single burning item*
- BS EN ISO 11925-2:2002, *Reaction to fire tests for building products,* Part 2 *Ignitability when subjected to direct impingement of flame.*

For some building products, there is currently no generally accepted guidance on the appropriate procedure for testing and classification in accordance with the harmonised European fire tests. Until such a time that the appropriate European test and classification methods for these building products are published classification may only be possible using existing national test methods.

Table A8, in Appendix A, gives typical performance ratings which may be achieved by some generic materials and products.

Section 3: Wall and ceiling linings

Classification of linings

3.1   Subject to the variations and specific provisions described in paragraphs 3.2 to 3.16, the surface linings of walls and ceilings should meet the following classifications:

Table 1 Classification of linings

Location	National class [1]	European class [1][3][4]
Small rooms [2] of area not more than 4m²	3	D-s3, d2
Domestic garages of area not more than 40m²		
Other rooms [2] (including garages)	1	C-s3, d2
Circulation spaces within dwellinghouses		

Notes:

1.   See paragraph B2.v.

2.   For meaning of room, see definition in Appendix E.

3.   The National classifications do not automatically equate with the equivalent classifications in the European column, therefore products cannot typically assume a European class, unless they have been tested accordingly.

4.   When a classification includes 's3, d2', this means that there is no limit set for smoke production and/or flaming droplets/particles.

Definition of walls

3.2   For the purpose of the performance of wall linings, a wall includes:

a.   the surface of glazing (except glazing in doors); and

b.   any part of a ceiling which slopes at an angle of more than 70° to the horizontal.

But a wall does not include:

c.   doors and door frames;

d.   window frames and frames in which glazing is fitted;

e.   architraves, cover moulds, picture rails, skirtings and similar narrow members; or

f.   fireplace surrounds, mantle shelves and fitted furniture.

Definition of ceilings

3.3   For the purposes of the performance of ceiling linings, a ceiling includes:

a.   the surface of glazing;

b.   any part of a wall which slopes at an angle of 70° or less to the horizontal;

c.   the underside of a gallery; and

d.   the underside of a roof exposed to the room below.

But a ceiling does not include:

e.   trap doors and their frames;

f.   the frames of windows or rooflights (see Appendix E) and frames in which glazing is fitted; or

g.   architraves, cover moulds, picture rails, exposed beams and similar narrow members.

Variations and special provisions

Walls

3.4   Parts of walls in rooms may be of a poorer performance than specified in paragraph 3.1 (but not poorer than Class 3 (National class) or Class D-s3, d2 (European class) provided the total area of those parts in any one room does not exceed one half of the floor area of the room, subject to a maximum of 20m².

Fire-protecting suspended ceilings

3.5   A suspended ceiling can contribute to the overall fire resistance of a floor/ceiling assembly. Such a ceiling should satisfy paragraph 3.1. It should also meet the provisions of Appendix A, Table A3.

Fire-resisting ceilings

3.6   Cavity barriers are needed in some concealed floor or roof spaces (see Section 6), however, this need can be reduced by the use of a fire-resisting ceiling below the cavity.

Rooflights

3.7   Rooflights should meet the relevant classification in 3.1. However, plastic rooflights with at least a Class 3 rating may be used where 3.1 calls for a higher standard, provided the limitations in Table 2 and in Table 6 are observed.

Note: No guidance is currently possible on the performance requirements in the European fire tests as there is no generally accepted test and classification procedure.

Thermoplastic materials

General

3.8   Thermoplastic materials (see Appendix A, paragraph 17) which cannot meet the performance given in Table 1, can nevertheless be used in windows, rooflights and lighting diffusers in suspended ceilings if they comply with the provisions described in paragraphs 3.10 to 3.14. Flexible thermoplastic material may be used in panels to form a suspended ceiling if it complies with the guidance in paragraph 3.16. The classifications used in paragraphs 3.11 to 3.16, Table 2 and Diagram 9 are explained in Appendix A, paragraph 20.

Note: No guidance is currently possible on the performance requirements in the European fire tests as there is no generally accepted test and classification procedure.

Windows and internal glazing

3.9 External windows to rooms (though not to circulation spaces) may be glazed with thermoplastic materials, if the material can be classified as a TP(a) rigid product.

Internal glazing should meet the provisions in paragraph 3.1.

Notes:

1. A 'wall' does not include glazing in a door (see paragraph 3.2).

2. Attention is drawn to the guidance on the safety of glazing in Approved Document N *Glazing – safety in relation to impact, opening and cleaning.*

Rooflights

3.10 Rooflights to rooms and circulation spaces (with the exception of protected stairways) may be constructed of a thermoplastic material if:

a. the lower surface has a TP(a) (rigid) or TP(b) classification

b. the size and disposition of the rooflights accords with the limits in Table 2 and with the guidance to B4 in Table 7.

Lighting diffusers

3.11 The following provisions apply to lighting diffusers which form part of a ceiling. They are not concerned with diffusers of light fittings which are attached to the soffit of, or suspended beneath a ceiling (see Diagram 8).

Lighting diffusers are translucent or open-structured elements that allow light to pass through. They may be part of a luminaire or used below rooflights or other sources of light.

3.12 Thermoplastic lighting diffusers should not be used in fire-protecting or fire-resisting ceilings, unless they have been satisfactorily tested as part of the ceiling system that is to be used to provide the appropriate fire protection.

3.13 Subject to the above paragraphs, ceilings to rooms and circulation spaces (but not protected stairways) may incorporate thermoplastic lighting diffusers if the following provisions are observed:

a. Wall and ceiling surfaces exposed within the space above the suspended ceiling (other than the upper surfaces of the thermoplastic panels) should comply with the general provisions of paragraph 3.1, according to the type of space below the suspended ceiling;

b. If the diffusers are of classification TP(a) (rigid), there are no restrictions on their extent;

c. If the diffusers are of classification TP(b), they should be limited in extent as indicated in Table 2 and Diagram 9.

Suspended or stretched-skin ceilings

3.14 The ceiling of a room may be constructed either as a suspended or stretched-skin membrane from panels of a thermoplastic material of the TP(a) flexible classification, provided that it is not part of a fire-resisting ceiling. Each panel should not exceed 5m^2 in area and should be supported on all its sides.

Diagram 8 **Lighting diffuser in relation to ceiling**

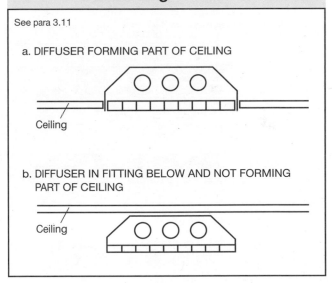

See para 3.11

a. DIFFUSER FORMING PART OF CEILING

Ceiling

b. DIFFUSER IN FITTING BELOW AND NOT FORMING PART OF CEILING

Ceiling

Table 2 Limitations applied to thermoplastic rooflights and lighting diffusers in suspended ceilings and Class 3 plastic rooflights

Minimum classification of lower surface	Use of space below the diffusers or rooflight	Maximum area of each diffuser panel or rooflight [1]	Max total area of diffuser panels and rooflights as percentage of floor area of the space in which the ceiling is located (%)	Minimum separation distance between diffuser panels or rooflights [1]
		(m²)		(m)
TP(a)	Any except protected stairway	No limit [2]	No limit	No limit
Class 3 [3] or TP(b)	Rooms	5	50 [4]	3
	Circulation spaces except protected stairways	5	15 [4]	3

Notes:

1. Smaller panels can be grouped together provided that the overall size of the group and the space between one group and any others satisfies the dimensions shown in Diagram 9.

2. Lighting diffusers of TP(a) flexible rating should be restricted to panels of not more than 5m² each, see paragraph 3.14.

3. There are no limits on Class 3 material in small rooms see Table 1.

4. The minimum 3m separation specified in Diagram 9 between each 5m² must be maintained. Therefore, in some cases it may not also be possible to use the maximum percentage quoted.

Diagram 9 Layout restrictions on Class 3 plastic rooflights, TP(b) rooflights and TP(b) lighting diffusers

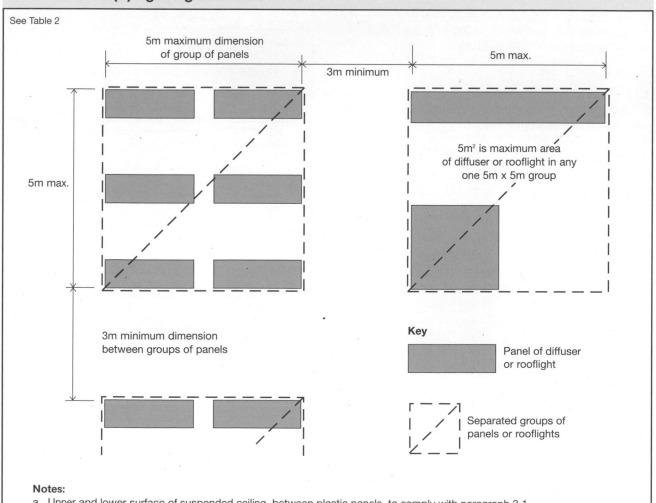

Notes:
a. Upper and lower surface of suspended ceiling, between plastic panels, to comply with paragraph 3.1.
b. No restriction on Class 3 rooflights in small rooms see Table 1.

The Requirement

This Approved Document deals with the following Requirement from Part B of Schedule 1 to the Building Regulations 2010.

Requirement	Limits on application
Internal fire spread (structure)	
B3. (1) The building shall be designed and constructed so that, in the event of fire, its stability will be maintained for a reasonable period.	
(2) A wall common to two or more buildings shall be designed and constructed so that it adequately resists the spread of fire between those buildings. For the purposes of this sub-paragraph a house in a terrace and a semi-detached house are each to be treated as a separate building.	
(3) Where reasonably necessary to inhibit the spread of fire within the building, measures shall be taken, to an extent appropriate to the size and intended use of the building, comprising either or both of the following:	Requirement B3(3) does not apply to material alterations to any prison provided under Section 33 of the Prison Act 1952.
(a) sub-division of the building with fire-resisting construction;	
(b) installation of suitable automatic fire suppression systems.	
(4) The building shall be designed and constructed so that the unseen spread of fire and smoke within concealed spaces in its structure and fabric is inhibited.	

Guidance

Performance

In the Secretary of State's view the Requirements of B3 will be met:

a. if the loadbearing elements of structure of the building are capable of withstanding the effects of fire for an appropriate period without loss of stability;

b. if the building is sub-divided by elements of fire-resisting construction into compartments;

c. if any openings in fire-separating elements (see Appendix E) are suitably protected in order to maintain the integrity of the element (i.e. the continuity of the fire separation); and

d. if any hidden voids in the construction are sealed and sub-divided to inhibit the unseen spread of fire and products of combustion, in order to reduce the risk of structural failure and the spread of fire, in so far as they pose a threat to the safety of people in and around the building.

The extent to which any of these measures are necessary is dependent on the use of the building and, in some cases, its size, and on the location of the element of construction.

Introduction

B3.i   Guidance on loadbearing elements of structure is given in Section 4. Section 5 is concerned with the sub-division of a building into compartments, and Section 6 makes provisions about concealed spaces (or cavities). Section 7 gives information on the protection of openings and on fire-stopping which relates to compartmentation and to fire spread in concealed spaces. Common to all these sections and to other provisions of Part B, is the property of fire resistance.

Fire resistance

B3.ii   The fire resistance of an element of construction is a measure of its ability to withstand the effects of fire in one or more ways, as follows:

a. resistance to collapse, i.e. the ability to maintain loadbearing capacity (which applies to loadbearing elements only);

b. resistance to fire penetration, i.e. an ability to maintain the integrity of the element; and

c. resistance to the transfer of excessive heat, i.e. an ability to provide insulation from high temperatures.

B3.iii   'Elements of structure' is the term applied to the main structural loadbearing elements, such as structural frames, floors and loadbearing walls. Compartment walls are treated as elements of structure although they are not necessarily loadbearing. Roofs, unless they serve the function of a floor, are not treated as elements of structure. External walls, such as curtain walls or other forms of cladding which transmit only self weight and wind loads and do not transmit floor load, are not regarded as loadbearing for the purposes of B3.ii(a), although they may need fire resistance to satisfy requirement B4 (see Sections 8 to 9).

Loadbearing elements may or may not have a fire-separating function. Similarly, fire-separating elements may or may not be loadbearing.

Guidance elsewhere in the Approved Document concerning fire resistance

B3.iv   There is guidance in Section 2 concerning the use of fire-resisting construction to protect means of escape. There is guidance in Section 9 about fire resistance of external walls to restrict the spread of fire between buildings. Appendix A gives information on methods of test and performance for elements of construction. Appendix B gives information on fire doors. Appendix C gives information on methods of measurement. Appendix D gives information on purpose group classification. Appendix E gives definitions.

Section 4: Loadbearing elements of structure

Introduction

4.1   Premature failure of the structure can be prevented by provisions for loadbearing elements of structure to have a minimum standard of fire resistance, in terms of resistance to collapse or failure of loadbearing capacity. The purpose in providing the structure with fire resistance is threefold, namely:

a.   to minimise the risk to the occupants, some of whom may be unable to make their own escape if they have become trapped or injured;

b.   to reduce the risk to firefighters, who may be engaged in search or rescue operations; and

c.   to reduce the danger to people in the vicinity of the building, who might be hurt by falling debris or as a result of the impact of the collapsing structure on other buildings.

Fire resistance standard

4.2   Elements of structure such as structural frames, beams, columns, loadbearing walls (internal and external), floor structures and gallery structures should have at least the fire resistance given in Appendix A, Table A1.

Application of the fire resistance standards for loadbearing elements

4.3   The measures set out in Appendix A include provisions to ensure that where one element of structure supports or gives stability to another element of structure, the supporting element has no less fire resistance than the other element (see notes to Table A2). The measures also provide for elements of structure that are common to more than one building or compartment, to be constructed to the standard of the greater of the relevant provisions. Special provisions about fire resistance of elements of structure in single storey buildings are also given and there are concessions in respect of fire resistance of elements of structure in basements where at least one side of the basement is open at ground level.

Exclusions from the provisions for elements of structure

4.4   The following are excluded from the definition of element of structure for the purposes of these provisions:

a.   structure that only supports a roof, unless:

   i.   the roof performs the function of a floor, such as a roof terrace, or as a means of escape (see Section 2), or

   ii.   the structure is essential for the stability of an external wall which needs to have fire resistance; and

b.   the lowest floor of the building.

Additional guidance

4.5   Guidance in other sections of this Approved Document may also apply if a loadbearing wall is:

a.   a compartment wall (this includes a wall common to two buildings), (see Section 5);

b.   a wall between a dwellinghouse and an integral garage, (see Section 5, paragraph 5.4);

c.   protecting a means of escape, (see Section 2); or

d.   an external wall, (see Sections 8 to 9).

4.6   If a floor is also a compartment floor, see Section 5.

Floors in loft conversions

4.7   In altering an existing two-storey single family dwellinghouse to provide additional storeys, the provisions in this Approved Document are for the floor(s), both old and new, to have the full 30 minute standard of fire resistance shown in Appendix A, Table A1. However, provided that the following conditions are satisfied, namely:

a.   only one storey is being added;

b.   the new storey contains no more than 2 habitable rooms; and

c.   the total area of the new storey does not amount to more than 50m^2;

then the existing first floor construction may be accepted if it has at least a modified 30 minute standard of fire resistance, in those places where the floor separates only rooms (and not circulation spaces).

Notes:

1.   The 'modified 30 minute' standard satisfies the test criteria for the full 30 minutes in respect of loadbearing capacity, but allows reduced performances for integrity and insulation (see Appendix A, Table A1, item 3(a)).

2.   A floor which forms part of the enclosure to the circulation space between the loft conversion and the final exit needs a full 30 minute standard.

Conversion to flats

4.8   Where an existing dwellinghouse or other building is converted into flats the guidance in Volume 2 should be followed.

Section 5: Compartmentation

Introduction

5.1 The spread of fire within a building can be restricted by sub-dividing it into compartments separated from one another by walls and/or floors of fire-resisting construction. The object is twofold:

a. to prevent rapid fire spread which could trap occupants of the building; and

b. to reduce the chance of fires becoming large, on the basis that large fires are more dangerous, not only to occupants and fire and rescue service personnel, but also to people in the vicinity of the building. Compartmentation is complementary to provisions made in Section 2 for the protection of escape routes, and to provisions made in Sections 8 to 10 against the spread of fire between buildings.

Provision of compartmentation

5.2 Compartment walls and compartment floors should be provided in the circumstances described below, with the proviso that the lowest floor in a building does not need to be constructed as a compartment floor. Provisions for the protection of openings in compartment walls and compartment floors are given in paragraph 5.13 and Section 7.

5.3 Every wall separating semi-detached houses, or houses in terraces, should be constructed as a compartment wall and the houses should be considered as separate buildings.

5.4 If a domestic garage is attached to (or forms an integral part of) a dwellinghouse, the garage should be separated from the rest of the dwellinghouse, as shown in Diagram 10.

5.5 Where a door is provided between a dwellinghouse and the garage, the floor of the garage should be laid to fall to allow fuel spills to flow away from the door to the outside. Alternatively, the door opening should be positioned at least 100mm above garage floor level.

Construction of compartment walls and compartment floors

General

5.6 Every compartment wall and compartment floor should:

a. form a complete barrier to fire between the compartments they separate; and

b. have the appropriate fire resistance as indicated in Appendix A, Tables A1 and A2.

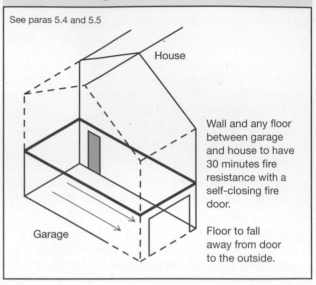

Diagram 10 **Separation between garage and dwellinghouse**

See paras 5.4 and 5.5

House

Garage

Wall and any floor between garage and house to have 30 minutes fire resistance with a self-closing fire door.

Floor to fall away from door to the outside.

Note: Timber beams, joists, purlins and rafters may be built into or carried through a masonry or concrete compartment wall if the openings for them are kept as small as practicable and then fire-stopped. If trussed rafters bridge the wall, they should be designed so that failure of any part of the truss due to a fire in one compartment will not cause failure of any part of the truss in another compartment.

Compartment walls between buildings

5.7 Compartment walls that are common to two or more buildings should run the full height of the building in a continuous vertical plane. Thus adjoining buildings should only be separated by walls, not floors.

5.8 Compartment walls in a top storey beneath a roof should be continued through the roof space (see definition of compartment in Appendix E).

Junction of compartment wall or compartment floor with other walls

5.9 Where a compartment wall or compartment floor meets another compartment wall, or an external wall, the junction should maintain the fire resistance of the compartmentation. Fire-stopping should meet the provisions of paragraphs 7.12 to 7.14.

5.10 At the junction of a compartment floor with an external wall that has no fire resistance (such as a curtain wall) the external wall should be restrained at floor level to reduce the movement of the wall away from the floor when exposed to fire.

Junction of compartment wall with roof

5.11   A compartment wall should be taken up to meet the underside of the roof covering or deck, with fire-stopping where necessary at the wall/roof junction to maintain the continuity of fire resistance. The compartment wall should also be continued across any eaves.

5.12   If a fire penetrates a roof near a compartment wall there is a risk that it will spread over the roof to the adjoining compartment. To reduce this risk either:

a.   the wall should be extended up through the roof for a height of at least 375mm above the top surface of the adjoining roof covering (see Diagram 11a). Where there is a height difference of at least 375mm between two roofs or where the roof coverings on either side of the wall are AA, AB or AC this height may be reduced to 200mm; or

b.   a zone of the roof 1500mm wide on either side of the wall should have a covering of designation AA, AB or AC. Any combustible boarding used as a substrate to the roof covering, wood wool slabs, or timber tiling battens that are carried over the compartment wall should be fully bedded in mortar or other suitable material over the width of the wall (see Diagram 11b).

Note: Double-skinned insulated roof sheeting with a thermoplastic core should incorporate a band of material of limited combustibility at least 300mm wide centred over the wall.

Openings in compartmentation

Openings in compartment walls separating buildings or occupancies

5.13   Any openings in a compartment wall which is common to two or more buildings should be limited to those for:

a.   a door which is needed to provide a means of escape in case of fire and which has the same fire resistance as that required for the wall (see Appendix B, Table B1) and is fitted in accordance with the provisions of Appendix B; and

b.   the passage of a pipe which meets the provisions in Section 7.

Doors

5.14   Information on fire doors may be found in Appendix B.

Diagram 11 Junction of compartment wall with roof

See para 5.11

a.

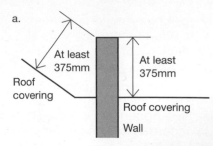

Roof covering · At least 375mm

At least 375mm

Roof covering

Wall

The wall should be extended up through the roof for a height of at least 375mm above the top surface of the adjoining roof covering.

Where there is a height difference of at least 375mm between two roofs or where the roof coverings on either side of the wall are AA, AB or AC the height of the upstand/parapet wall above the highest roof may be reduced to 200mm.

b.

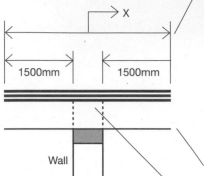

X

1500mm · 1500mm

Wall

X

Section X–X

Roof covering to be designated AA, AB or AC for at least this distance.

Boarding (used as a substrate), wood wool slabs or timber tiling battens may be carried over the wall provided that they are fully bedded in mortar (or other no less suitable material) where over the wall.

Thermoplastic insulation materials should not be carried over the wall.

Double-skinned insulated roof sheeting with a thermoplastic core should incorporate a band of material of limited combustibility at least 300mm wide centred over the wall.

Sarking felt may also be carried over the wall.

If roof support members pass through the wall, fire protection to these members for a distance of 1500mm on either side of the wall may be needed to delay distortion at the junction (see note to paragraph 5.6).

Fire-stopping to be carried up to underside of roof covering, boarding or slab.

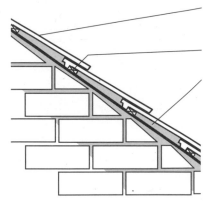

Roof covering to be designated AA, AB or AC for at least 1500mm either side of wall.

Roofing battens and sarking felt may be carried over the wall.

Fire-stopping to be carried up to underside of roof covering. Above and below sarking felt.

Notes
1 Fire-stopping should be carried over the full thickness of the wall.
2 Fire-stopping should be extended into any eaves.
3 The compartment wall need not necessarily be constructed of masonry.

Section 6: Concealed spaces (cavities)

Introduction

6.1 Concealed spaces or cavities in the construction of a building provide a ready route for smoke and flame spread e.g. in walls, floors, ceilings and roofs. As any spread is concealed, it presents a greater danger than would a more obvious weakness in the fabric of the building.

Provision of cavity barriers

6.2 Provisions are given below for cavity barriers in specified locations. The provisions necessary to restrict the spread of smoke and flames through cavities are broadly for the purpose of sub-dividing cavities, which could otherwise form a pathway around a fire separating element, and closing the edges of cavities; therefore reducing the potential for unseen fire spread. See also paragraph 2.14.

Note: These should not be confused with fire stopping details, see Sections 5 and 7.

Consideration should also be given to the construction and fixing of cavity barriers provided for these purposes and the extent to which openings in them should be protected. For guidance on these issues, see paragraphs 6.6 to 6.9 respectively.

6.3 Cavity barriers should be provided at the edges of cavities, including around openings (such as window and door openings). Additionally, cavity barriers should be provided at the junction between an external cavity wall and a compartment wall that separates buildings, see Diagram 12; and at the top of such an external cavity wall, except where the cavity wall complies with Diagram 13.

Diagram 12 Interrupting concealed spaces (cavities)

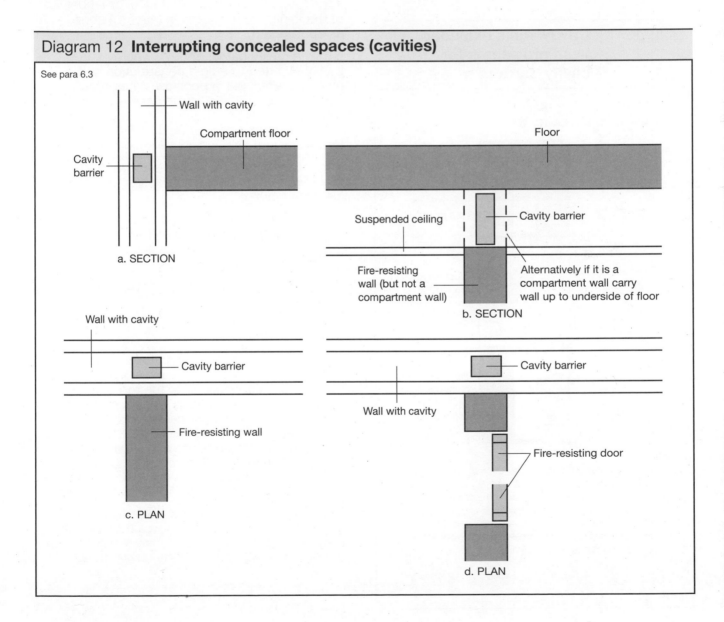

It is important to continue any compartment wall up through a ceiling or roof cavity to maintain the standard of fire resistance – therefore compartment walls should be carried up to the roof, see paragraph 5.11. It is not appropriate to complete a line of compartment walls by fitting cavity barriers above them.

Double-skinned insulated roof sheeting

6.4 Cavity barriers need not be provided between double-skinned corrugated or profiled insulated roof sheeting, if the sheeting is a material of limited combustibility; and both surfaces of the insulating layer have a surface spread of flame of at least Class 0 or 1 (National class) or Class C-s3, d2 or better (European class) (see Appendix A); and make contact with the inner and outer skins of cladding.

Note: When a classification includes "s3, d2", this means that there is no limit set for smoke production and/or flaming droplets/particles.

Diagram 13 Cavity walls excluded from provisions for cavity barriers

See para 6.3

SECTION THROUGH CAVITY WALL

Close cavity at top of wall (unless cavity is totally filled with insulation)

Opening

Close cavity around opening

Two leaves of brick or concrete each at least 75mm thick

Note:

1 Domestic meter cupboards may be installed provided that:
 a) there are no more than two cupboards per dwelling.
 b) the openings in the outer wall leaf is not more than 800–500mm for each cupboard.
 c) the inner leaf is not penetrated except by a sleeve not more than 80x80mm, which is fire-stopped.

2 Combustible materials may be placed within the cavity.

Construction and fixings for cavity barriers

6.5 Every cavity barrier should be constructed to provide at least 30 minutes fire resistance and may be formed by any construction provided for another purpose if it meets the provisions for cavity barriers (see Appendix A, Table A1, item 10).

However, cavity barriers in a stud wall or partition, or provided around openings may be formed of:

a. steel at least 0.5mm thick; or

b. timber at least 38mm thick; or

c. polythene-sleeved mineral wool, or mineral wool slab, in either case under compression when installed in the cavity; or

d. calcium silicate, cement-based or gypsum-based boards at least 12mm thick.

Note: Cavity barriers provided around openings may be formed by the window or door frame if the frame is constructed of steel or timber of the minimum thickness in (a) or (b) above as appropriate.

6.6 A cavity barrier should, wherever possible, be tightly fitted to a rigid construction and mechanically fixed in position. Where this is not possible (for example, in the case of a junction with slates, tiles, corrugated sheeting or similar materials) the junction should be fire-stopped. Provisions for fire-stopping are set out in Section 7.

6.7 Cavity barriers should also be fixed so that their performance is unlikely to be made ineffective by:

a. movement of the building due to subsidence, shrinkage or temperature change; and movement of the external envelope due to wind; and

b. collapse in a fire of any services penetrating them; and

c. failure in a fire of their fixings (but see note below); and

d. failure in a fire of any material or construction which they abut. (For example, if a suspended ceiling is continued over the top of a fire-resisting wall or partition, and direct connection is made between the ceiling and the cavity barrier above the line of the wall or partition, premature failure of the cavity barrier can occur when the ceiling collapses. However, this may not arise if the ceiling is designed to provide fire resistance of 30 minutes or more.)

Note: Where cavity barriers are provided in roof spaces, the roof members to which they are fitted are not expected to have any fire resistance (for the purpose of supporting the cavity barrier(s)).

Openings in cavity barriers

6.8 Any openings in a cavity barrier should be limited to those for:

a. doors which have at least 30 minutes fire resistance (see Appendix B, Table B1, item 1(a)) and are fitted in accordance with the provisions of Appendix B;

b. the passage of pipes which meet the provisions in Section 7;

c. the passage of cables or conduits containing one or more cables;

d. openings fitted with a suitably mounted automatic fire damper; and

e. ducts which are fire-resisting or are fitted with a suitably mounted automatic fire damper where they pass through the cavity barrier.

Section 7: Protection of openings and fire-stopping

Introduction

7.1   Sections 7 and 8 make provisions for fire-separating elements and set out the circumstances in which there may be openings in them. This section deals with the protection of openings in such elements.

7.2   If a fire-separating element is to be effective, then every joint, or imperfection of fit, or opening to allow services to pass through the element, should be adequately protected by sealing or fire-stopping so that the fire resistance of the element is not impaired.

7.3   The measures in this section are intended to delay the passage of fire. They generally have the additional benefit of retarding smoke spread but the test specified in Appendix A for integrity does not directly stipulate criteria for the passage of smoke.

7.4   Consideration should also be given to the effect of services that may be built into the construction that could adversely affect its fire resistance. For instance, where downlighters, loudspeakers and other electrical accessories are installed, additional protection may be required to maintain the integrity of a wall or floor.

7.5   Detailed guidance on door openings and fire doors is given in Appendix B.

Openings for pipes

7.6   Pipes which pass through fire-separating elements (unless the pipe is in a protected shaft), should meet the appropriate provisions in alternatives A, B or C below.

Alternative A: Proprietary seals (any pipe diameter)

7.7   Provide a proprietary sealing system which has been shown by test to maintain the fire resistance of the wall, floor or cavity barrier.

Alternative B: Pipes with a restricted diameter

7.8   Where a proprietary sealing system is not used, fire-stopping may be used around the pipe, keeping the opening as small as possible. The nominal internal diameter of the pipe should not be more than the relevant dimension given in Table 3.

Table 3   Maximum nominal internal diameter of pipes passing through a fire separating element (see paragraph 7.6 to 7.9)

Situation	Pipe material and maximum nominal internal diameter (mm)		
	(a) Non-combustible material [1]	(b) Lead, aluminium, aluminium alloy, uPVC [2], fibre cement	(c) Any other material
1. Wall separating dwellinghouses	160	160 (stack pipe) [3] 110 (branch pipe) [3]	40
2. Wall or floor separating a dwellinghouse from an attached garage	160	110	40
3. Any other situation	160	40	40

Notes:

1.   Any non-combustible material (such as cast iron, copper or steel) which, if exposed to a temperature of 800°C, will not soften or fracture to the extent that flame or hot gas will pass through the wall of the pipe.

2.   uPVC pipes complying with BS 4514 and uPVC pipes complying with BS 5255.

3.   These diameters are only in relation to pipes forming part of an above-ground drainage system and enclosed as shown in Diagram 15. In other cases the maximum diameters against situation 3 apply.

Alternative C: sleeving

7.9   A pipe of lead, aluminium, aluminium alloy, fibre-cement or uPVC, with a maximum nominal internal diameter of 160mm, may be used with a sleeving of non-combustible pipe as shown in Diagram 14. The specification for non-combustible and uPVC pipes is given in the notes to Table 3.

Diagram 14 Pipes penetrating structure

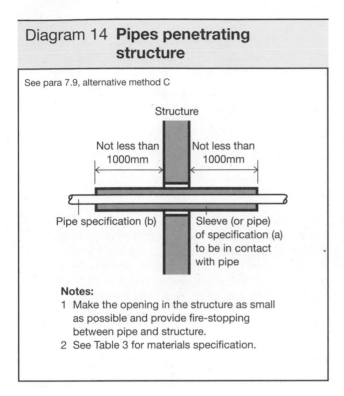

See para 7.9, alternative method C

Notes:

1 Make the opening in the structure as small as possible and provide fire-stopping between pipe and structure.

2 See Table 3 for materials specification.

Diagram 15 Enclosure for drainage or water supply pipes

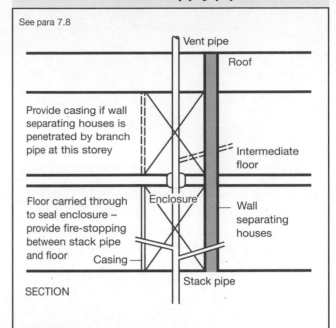

See para 7.8

SECTION

Notes:

1 The enclosure should:
   a. be bounded by a compartment wall or floor, an outside wall, an intermediate floor, or a casing (see specification at 2 below);
   b. have internal surfaces (except framing members) of Class 0 (National class) or Class B-s3, d2 or better (European class) Note: When a classification includes 's3, d2', this means that there is no limit set for smoke production and/or flaming droplets/particles);
   c. not have an access panel which opens into a circulation space or bedroom;
   d. be used only for drainage, or water supply, or vent pipes for a drainage system.

2 The casing should:
   a. be imperforate except for an opening for a pipe or an access panel;
   b. not be of sheet metal;
   c. have (including any access panel) not less than 30 minutes fire resistance.

3 The opening for a pipe, either in the structure or the casing, should be as small as possible and fire-stopped around the pipe.

Ventilation ducts, flues etc.

7.10   Air circulation systems which circulate air within an individual dwellinghouse with a floor more than 4.5m above ground level should meet the guidance given in paragraph 2.16. Where ventilation ducts pass through compartment walls into another building then the guidance given in Approved Document B Volume 2 should be followed.

Diagram 16 Flues penetrating compartment walls or floors
(note that there is guidance in Approved Document J concerning hearths adjacent to compartment walls)

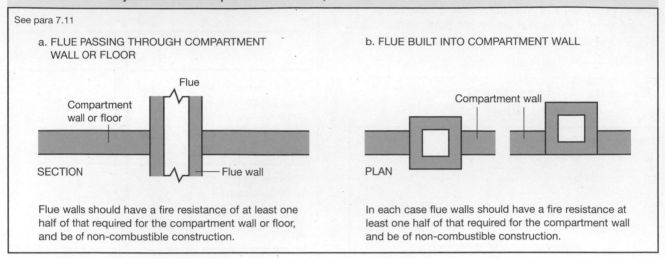

See para 7.11

a. FLUE PASSING THROUGH COMPARTMENT WALL OR FLOOR

Flue

Compartment wall or floor

SECTION

Flue wall

Flue walls should have a fire resistance of at least one half of that required for the compartment wall or floor, and be of non-combustible construction.

b. FLUE BUILT INTO COMPARTMENT WALL

Compartment wall

PLAN

In each case flue walls should have a fire resistance at least one half of that required for the compartment wall and be of non-combustible construction.

7.11 If a flue or duct containing flues or appliance ventilation duct(s), passes through a compartment wall or compartment floor, or is built into a compartment wall, each wall of the flue or duct should have a fire resistance of at least half that of the wall or floor in order to prevent the by-passing of the compartmentation (see Diagram 16).

Fire-stopping

7.12 In addition to any other provisions in this document for fire-stopping:

a. joints between fire-separating elements should be fire-stopped; and

b. all openings for pipes, ducts, conduits or cables to pass through any part of a fire-separating element should be:

   i. kept as few in number as possible; and

   ii. kept as small as practicable; and

   iii. fire-stopped (which in the case of a pipe or duct should allow thermal movement).

7.13 To prevent displacement, materials used for fire-stopping should be reinforced with (or supported by) materials of limited combustibility in the following circumstances:

a. in all cases where the unsupported span is greater than 100mm; and

b. in any other case where non-rigid materials are used (unless they have been shown to be satisfactory by test).

7.14 Proprietary fire-stopping and sealing systems, (including those designed for service penetrations) which have been shown by test to maintain the fire resistance of the wall or other element, are available and may be used.

Other fire-stopping materials include:

* cement mortar;

* gypsum-based plaster;

* cement-based or gypsum-based vermiculite/perlite mixes;

* glass fibre, crushed rock, blast furnace slag or ceramic-based products (with or without resin binders); and

* intumescent mastics.

These may be used in situations appropriate to the particular material. Not all of them will be suitable in every situation.

Guidance on the process of design, installation and maintenance of passive fire protection is available in *Ensuring Best Practice for Passive Fire Protection in Buildings* (ISBN: 1 87040 919 1) produced by the Association for Specialist Fire Protection (ASFP).

Further information on the generic types of systems available, information about their suitability for different applications and guidance on test methods is given in the ASFP Red Book: *Fire Stopping and Penetration Seals for the Construction Industry – the 'Red Book'* published by the Association for Specialist Fire Protection and freely available from the ASFP website at www.asfp.org.uk.

The Requirement

This Approved Document deals with the
following Requirement from Part B of Schedule 1
to the Building Regulations 2010.

Requirement	Limits on application
External fire spread	
B4. (1) The external walls of the building shall adequately resist the spread of fire over the walls and from one building to another, having regard to the height, use and position of the building.	
(2) The roof of the building shall adequately resist the spread of fire over the roof and from one building to another, having regard to the use and position of the building.	

Guidance

Performance

In the Secretary of State's view the Requirements of B4 will be met:

a. if the external walls are constructed so that the risk of ignition from an external source, and the spread of fire over their surfaces, is restricted by making provision for them to have low rates of heat release;

b. if the amount of unprotected area in the side of the building is restricted so as to limit the amount of thermal radiation that can pass through the wall, taking the distance between the wall and the boundary into account; and

c. if the roof is constructed so that the risk of spread of flame and/or fire penetration from an external fire source is restricted.

In each case so as to limit the risk of a fire spreading from the building to a building beyond the boundary, or vice versa.

The extent to which this is necessary is dependent on the use of the building, its distance from the boundary and, in some cases, its height.

Introduction

External walls

B4.i   The construction of external walls and the separation between buildings to prevent external fire spread are closely related.

The chances of fire spreading across an open space between buildings, and the consequences if it does, depend on:

a. the size and intensity of the fire in the building concerned;

b. the distance between the buildings;

c. the fire protection given by their facing sides; and

d. the risk presented to people in the other building(s).

B4.ii   Provisions are made in Section 8 for the fire resistance of external walls and to limit the susceptibility of the external surface of walls to ignition and to fire spread.

B4.iii   Provisions are made in Section 9 to limit the extent of openings and other unprotected areas in external walls in order to reduce the risk of fire spread by radiation.

Roofs

B4.iv   Provisions are made in Section 10 for reducing the risk of fire spread between roofs and over the surfaces of roofs.

Section 8: Construction of external walls

Introduction

8.1   Provisions are made in this section for the external walls of the building to have sufficient fire resistance to prevent fire spread across the relevant boundary. The provisions are closely linked with those for space separation in Section 9 which sets out limits on the amount of unprotected area of wall. As the limits depend on the distance of the wall from the relevant boundary, it is possible for some or all of the walls to have no fire resistance, except for any parts which are loadbearing (see paragraph B3.iii).

External walls are elements of structure and the relevant period of fire resistance (specified in Appendix A) depends on the use, height and size of the building concerned. If the wall is 1000mm or more from the relevant boundary, a reduced standard of fire resistance is accepted in most cases and the wall only needs fire resistance from the inside.

8.2   Provisions are also made to restrict the combustibility of external walls of buildings that are less than 1000mm from the relevant boundary. This is in order to reduce the surface's susceptibility to ignition from an external source.

In the guidance to Requirement B3, provisions are made in Section 4 for internal and external loadbearing walls to maintain their loadbearing function in the event of fire.

Fire resistance standard

8.3   The external walls of the building should have the appropriate fire resistance given in Appendix A, Table A1, unless they form an unprotected area under the provisions of Section 9.

External surfaces

8.4   The external surfaces of walls within 1000mm of the relevant boundary should meet Class 0 (National Class) or Class B-s3,d2 or better (European class). The total amount of combustible material on walls more than 1000mm from the relevant boundary may be limited in practice by the provisions for space separation in Section 9 (see paragraphs 9.7 to 9.17.).

Section 9: Space separation

Introduction

9.1　The provisions in this Section are based on a number of assumptions and, whilst some of these may differ from the circumstances of a particular case, together they enable a reasonable standard of space separation to be specified. The provisions limit the extent of unprotected areas in the sides of a building (such as openings and areas with a combustible surface) which will not give adequate protection against the external spread of fire from one building to another.

A roof is not subject to the provisions in this Section unless it is pitched at an angle greater than 70° to the horizontal (see definition for 'external wall' in Appendix E). Similarly, vertical parts of a pitched roof such as dormer windows (which taken in isolation might be regarded as a wall), would not need to meet the following provisions unless the slope of the roof exceeds 70°. It is a matter of judgement whether a continuous run of dormer windows occupying most of a steeply pitched roof should be treated as a wall rather than a roof.

9.2　The assumptions are:

a. that the size of a fire will depend on the compartmentation of the building, so that a fire may involve a complete compartment, but will not spread to other compartments;

b. that the intensity of the fire is related to the use of the building (i.e. purpose group), but that it can be moderated by a sprinkler system;

c. that Residential (1 and 2) and Assembly and Recreation (5) Purpose Groups represent a greater life risk than other uses;

d. that there is a building on the far side of the boundary that has a similar elevation to the one in question and that it is at the same distance from the common boundary; and

e. that the amount of radiation that passes through any part of the external wall that has fire resistance may be discounted.

9.3　Where a reduced separation distance is desired (or an increased amount of unprotected area) it may be advantageous to introduce additional compartment walls and/or floors.

Boundaries

9.4　The use of the distance to a boundary, rather than to another building, in measuring the separation distance, makes it possible to calculate the allowable proportion of unprotected areas, regardless of whether there is a building on an adjoining site and regardless of the site of that building and the extent of any unprotected areas that it might have.

A wall is treated as facing a boundary if it makes an angle with it of 80° or less (see Diagram 17).

Usually only the distance to the actual boundary of the site needs to be considered. But, in some circumstances, when the site boundary adjoins a space where further development is unlikely, such as a road, then part of the adjoining space may be included as falling within the relevant boundary for the purposes of this section. The meaning of the term boundary is explained in Diagram 17.

Relevant boundaries

9.5　The boundary which a wall faces, whether it is the actual boundary of the site or a notional boundary, is called the relevant boundary (see Diagrams 17 and 18).

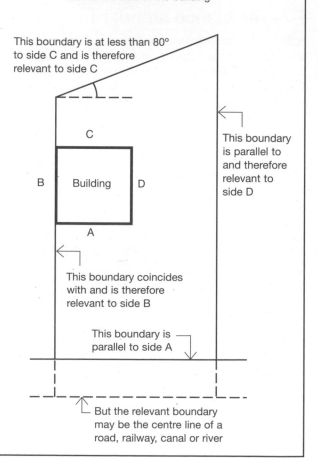

Diagram 17　**Relevant boundary**

See paras 9.4 and 9.5

This diagram sets out the rules that apply in respect of a boundary for it to be considered as a relevant boundary.

For a boundary to be relevant it should:
a. coincide with; or
b. be parallel to; or
c. be at an angle of not more than 80° to the side of the building

This boundary is at less than 80° to side C and is therefore relevant to side C

C

B　Building　D

A

This boundary is parallel to and therefore relevant to side D

This boundary coincides with and is therefore relevant to side B

This boundary is parallel to side A

But the relevant boundary may be the centre line of a road, railway, canal or river

Notional boundaries

9.6 The distances to other buildings on the same site also need to be considered. This is done by assuming that there is a boundary between those buildings. This assumed boundary is called a notional boundary. The appropriate rules are given in Diagram 18.

Unprotected areas

Unprotected areas and fire resistance

9.7 Any part of an external wall which has less fire resistance than the appropriate amount given in Appendix A, Table A2, is considered to be an unprotected area.

Status of combustible surface materials as unprotected area

9.8 If an external wall has the appropriate fire resistance, but has combustible material more than 1mm thick as its external surface, then that wall is counted as an unprotected area amounting to half the actual area of the combustible material, see Diagram 19. (For the purposes of this provision, a material with a Class 0 rating (National class) or Class B-s3, d2 rating (European class) (see Appendix A, paragraphs 7 and 13) need not be counted as unprotected area.)

Note: When a classification includes 's3, d2', this means that there is no limit set for smoke production and/or flaming droplets/particles.

Diagram 19 Status of combustible surface material as unprotected area

See para 9.8

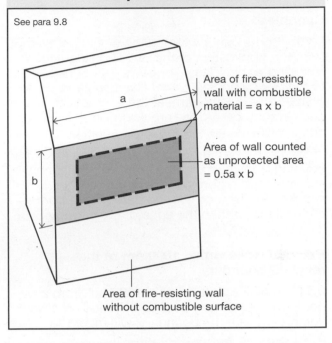

Area of fire-resisting wall with combustible material = a x b

Area of wall counted as unprotected area = 0.5a x b

Area of fire-resisting wall without combustible surface

Diagram 18 Notional boundary

See para 9.6

This diagram sets out the rules that apply where there is a building on the same site so that a notional boundary needs to be assumed between the buildings.

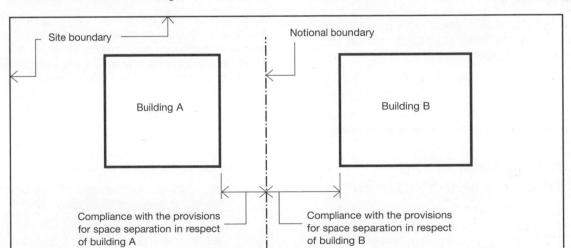

Site boundary

Notional boundary

Building A

Building B

Compliance with the provisions for space separation in respect of building A

Compliance with the provisions for space separation in respect of building B

The notional boundary should be set in the area between the two buildings using the following rules:
1. The notional boundary is assumed to exist in the space between the buildings and is positioned so that one of the buildings would comply with the provisions for space separation having regard to the amount of its unprotected area. In practice, if one of the buildings is existing, the position of the boundary will be set by the space separation factors for that building.
2. The siting of the new building, or the second building if both are new, can then be checked to see that it also complies, using the notional boundary as the relevant boundary for the second building.

Small unprotected areas

9.9 Small unprotected areas in an otherwise protected area of wall are considered to pose a negligible risk of fire spread and may be disregarded. Diagram 20 shows the constraints that apply to the placing of such areas in relation to each other and to lines of compartmentation inside the building. These constraints vary according to the size of each unprotected area.

Canopies

9.10 Some canopy structures would be exempt from the application of the Building Regulations by falling within Class 6 or Class 7 of Schedule 2 to the Regulations *(Exempt Buildings and Work)*. Many others may not meet the exemption criteria and, in such cases, the provisions in this section about limits of unprotected areas could be onerous.

In the case of a canopy attached to the side of a building, provided that the edges of the canopy are at least 2m from the relevant boundary, separation distance may be determined from the wall rather than the edge of the canopy (see Diagram 21).

External walls within 1000mm of the relevant boundary

9.11 A wall situated within 1000mm from any point on the relevant boundary, including a wall coincident with the boundary, will meet the provisions for space separation if:

a. the only unprotected areas are those shown in Diagram 20; and

b. the rest of the wall is fire-resisting from both sides.

External walls 1000mm or more from the relevant boundary

9.12 A wall situated at least 1000mm from any point on the relevant boundary will meet the provisions for space separation if:

a. the extent of unprotected area does not exceed that given by one of the methods referred to in paragraph 9.13; and

b. the rest of the wall (if any) is fire-resisting.

Methods for calculating acceptable unprotected area

9.13 Two simple methods are given in this Approved Document for calculating the acceptable amount of unprotected area in an external wall that is at least 1000mm from any point on the relevant boundary. (For walls within 1000mm of the boundary see paragraph 9.11 above.)

Method 1 may be used for small residential buildings and is set out in paragraph 9.16.

Method 2 may be used for most buildings or compartments for which Method 1 is not appropriate, and is set out in paragraph 9.17.

There are other more precise methods, described in a BRE report *External fire spread: Building separation and boundary distances* (BR 187, BRE 1991), which may be used instead of Methods 1 and 2. The 'Enclosing Rectangle' and 'Aggregate Notional Area' methods are included in the BRE report.

Basis for calculating acceptable unprotected area

9.14 The basis of Methods 1 and 2 was originally set out in Fire Research Technical Paper No 5, 1963. This has been reprinted as part of the BRE report referred to in paragraph 9.13. The aim is to ensure that the building is separated from the boundary by at least half the distance at which the total thermal radiation intensity received from all unprotected areas in the wall would be 12.6 kw/m^2 (in still air), assuming the radiation intensity at each unprotected area is 84 kw/m^2.

Sprinkler systems

9.15 If a building is fitted throughout with a sprinkler system, it is reasonable to assume that the intensity and extent of a fire will be reduced. The sprinkler system should meet the relevant recommendations of BS 9251 *Sprinkler systems for residential and domestic occupancies. Code of practice.* In these circumstances the boundary distance may be half that for an otherwise similar, but unsprinklered, building, subject to there being a minimum distance of 1000mm. Alternatively, the amount of unprotected area may be doubled if the boundary distance is maintained.

Note: The presence of sprinklers may be taken into account in a similar way when using the BRE report referred to in paragraph 9.14.

Method 1

9.16 This method applies only to a building, which is 1000mm or more from any point on the relevant boundary and meets the following rules for determining the maximum unprotected area, which should be read with Diagram 22:

a. The building should not exceed 3 storeys in height (basements are not counted) or be more than 24m in length; and

b. Each side of the building will meet the provisions for space separation if:

　i. the distance of the side of the building from the relevant boundary; and

　ii the extent of the unprotected area, are within the limits given in Diagram 22; and

　Note: In calculating the maximum unprotected area, any areas falling within the limits shown in Diagram 20, and referred to in paragraph 9.9, can be disregarded.

c. Any parts of the side of the building in excess of the maximum unprotected area should be fire-resisting.

Diagram 20 Unprotected areas which may be disregarded in assessing the separation distance from the boundary

See para 9.9

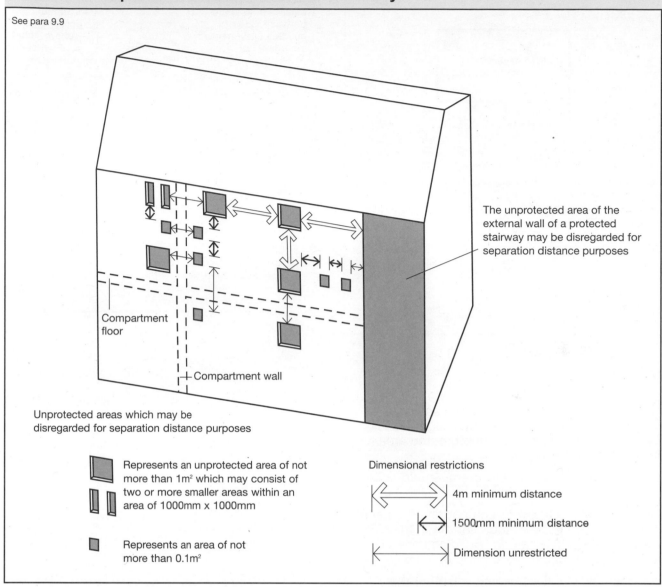

The unprotected area of the external wall of a protected stairway may be disregarded for separation distance purposes

Compartment floor

Compartment wall

Unprotected areas which may be disregarded for separation distance purposes

Represents an unprotected area of not more than 1m² which may consist of two or more smaller areas within an area of 1000mm x 1000mm

Represents an area of not more than 0.1m²

Dimensional restrictions

4m minimum distance

1500mm minimum distance

Dimension unrestricted

Diagram 21 The effect of a canopy on separation distance

See para 9.10

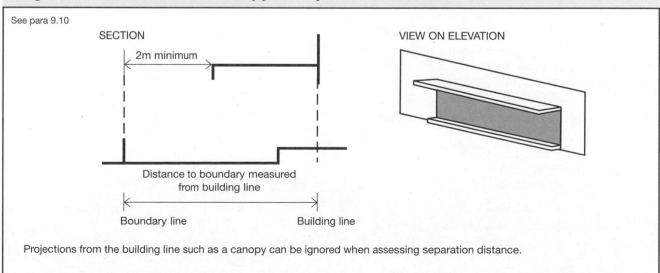

SECTION

2m minimum

Distance to boundary measured from building line

Boundary line

Building line

VIEW ON ELEVATION

Projections from the building line such as a canopy can be ignored when assessing separation distance.

Diagram 22 Permitted unprotected areas for Method 1

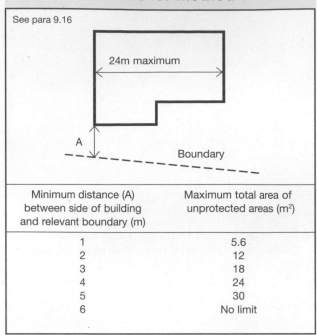

See para 9.16

24m maximum

A

Boundary

Minimum distance (A) between side of building and relevant boundary (m)	Maximum total area of unprotected areas (m²)
1	5.6
2	12
3	18
4	24
5	30
6	No limit

Table 4 Permitted unprotected areas for Method 2

Minimum distance between side of building and relevant boundary (m)	Maximum total percentage of unprotected area %
1	8
2.5	20
5	40
7.5	60
10	80
12.5	100

Notes:

a.   Intermediate values may be obtained by interpolation.

b.   For buildings which are fitted throughout with an automatic sprinkler system, see para 9.15.

c.   The total percentage of unprotected area is found by dividing the total unprotected area by the area of rectangle that encloses all the unprotected areas and multiplying the result by 100.

Method 2

9.17   This method applies to a dwellinghouse which is more than 1000mm from any point on the relevant boundary. The following rules for determining the maximum unprotected area should be read with Table 4.

a.   The building or compartment should not exceed 10m in height.

Note: For any building or compartment more than 10m in height, the methods set out in the BRE report *External fire spread: Building separation and boundary distances* can be applied.

b.   Each side of the building will meet the provisions for space separation if either:

i.   the distance of the side of the building from the relevant boundary; or

ii.   the extent of unprotected area, are within the appropriate limits given in Table 4.

Note: In calculating the maximum unprotected area, any areas shown in Diagram 20, and referred to in paragraph 9.9, can be disregarded.

c.   Any parts of the side of the building in excess of the maximum unprotected area should be fire-resisting.

Section 10: Roof coverings

Introduction

10.1   The provisions in this section limit the use, near a boundary, of roof coverings which will not give adequate protection against the spread of fire over them. The term roof covering is used to describe constructions which may consist of one or more layers of material, but does not refer to the roof structure as a whole. The provisions in this Section are principally concerned with the performance of roofs when exposed to fire from the outside.

10.2   The circumstances when a roof is subject to the provisions in Section 9 for space separation are explained in paragraph 9.1.

Other controls on roofs

10.3   There are provisions concerning the fire properties of roofs in other Sections of this document. In the guidance to B1 (paragraph 2.10) there are provisions for roofs that are part of a means of escape. In the guidance to B2 there are provisions for the internal surfaces of rooflights as part of the internal lining of a room or circulation space. In the guidance to B3 there are provisions in Section 4 for roofs which are used as a floor and in Section 6 for roofs that pass over the top of a compartment wall.

Classification of performance

10.4   The performance of roof coverings is designated by reference to the test methods specified in BS 476-3:2004 *Fire tests on building materials and structures. Classification and method of test for external fire exposure to roofs* or determined in accordance with BS EN 13501-5:2005 *Fire classification of construction products and building elements. Classification using data from external fire exposure to roof tests,* as described in Appendix A. The notional performance of some common roof coverings is given in Table A5 of Appendix A.

Rooflights are controlled on a similar basis, and plastic rooflights described in paragraphs 10.6 and 10.7 may also be used.

Separation distances

10.5   The separation distance is the minimum distance from the roof (or part of the roof) to the relevant boundary, which may be a notional boundary.

Table 5 sets out separation distances according to the type of roof covering and the size and use of the building. There are no restrictions on the use of roof coverings designated AA, AB or AC (National class) or B_{ROOF}(t4) (European class) classification. In addition, roof covering products (and/or materials) as defined in Commission Decision 2000/553/EC of 6 September 2000 implementing Council Directive 89/106/EEC

as regards the external fire performance of roof coverings can be considered to fulfil all of the requirements for performance characteristic 'external fire performance' without the need for testing **provided that any national provisions on the design and execution of works are fulfilled**.

Note: The boundary formed by the wall separating a pair of semi-detached houses may be disregarded for the purposes of this Section (but see Section 5, Diagram 11(b), which deals with roofs passing over the top of a compartment wall).

Plastic rooflights

10.6   Table 6 sets out the limitations on the use of plastic rooflights which have at least a Class 3 (National class) or Class D-s3, d2 (European class) lower surface, and Table 7 sets out the limitations on the use of thermoplastic materials with a TP(a) rigid or TP(b) classification (see also Diagram 23). The method of classifying thermoplastic materials is given in Appendix A.

Diagram 23 **Limitations on spacing and size of plastic rooflights having a Class 3 (National class) or Class D-s3, d2 (European class) or TP(b) lower surface**

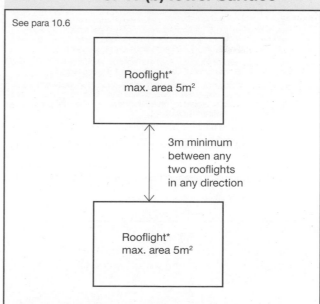

See para 10.6

Rooflight*
max. area 5m²

3m minimum between any two rooflights in any direction

Rooflight*
max. area 5m²

*or group of rooflights amounting to no more than 5m²

Notes:
1 There are restrictions on the use of plastic rooflights in the guidance to B2.
2 Surrounding roof covering to be a material of limited combustibility for at least 3m distance.
3 Where Diagram 11b applies, rooflights should be at least 1500mm from the compartment wall.

10.7   When used in rooflights, a rigid thermoplastic sheet product made from polycarbonate or from unplasticised PVC, which achieves a Class 1 (National class) rating for surface spread of flame when tested to BS 476-7:1997 (or 1987 or 1971), or Class C-s3,d2 (European class) can be regarded as having an AA (National class) designation or $B_{ROOF}(t4)$ (European class) classification, other than for the purposes of Diagram 11.

Unwired glass in rooflights

10.8   When used in rooflights, unwired glass at least 4mm thick can be regarded as having an AA designation (National class) or $B_{ROOF}(t4)$ (European class) classification.

Thatch and wood shingles

10.9   Thatch and wood shingles should be regarded as having an AD/BD/CD designation or $E_{ROOF}(t4)$ (European class) classification in Table 5 if performance under BS 476-3:2004 (or 1958) or BS EN 1187:xxxx cannot be established.

Note: Consideration can be given to thatched roofs being closer to the boundary than shown in Table 5 if, for example, the following precautions (based on *Thatched buildings. New properties and extensions* [the 'Dorset Model']) are incorporated in the design:

a.   the rafters are overdrawn with construction having not less than 30 minutes fire resistance;

b.   the guidance given in Approved Document J *Combustion appliances and fuel storage* is followed; and

c.   the smoke alarm installation (see Section 1) extends to the roof space.

Table 5   Limitations on roof coverings*

Designation† of covering of roof or part of roof		Minimum distance from any point on relevant boundary			
National Class	**European Class**	**Less than 6m**	**At least 6m**	**At least 12m**	**At least 20m**
AA, AB or AC	$B_{ROOF}(t4)$	●	●	●	●
BA, BB or BC	$C_{ROOF}(t4)$	○	●	●	●
CA, CB or CC	$D_{ROOF}(t4)$	○	●(1)(2)	●(1)	●
AD, BD or CD	$E_{ROOF}(t4)$	○	●(1)(2)	●(1)	●(1)
DA, DB, DC or DD	$F_{ROOF}(t4)$	○	○	○	●(1)(2)

Notes:

*   See paragraph 10.8 for limitations on glass; paragraph 10.9 for limitations on thatch and wood shingles; and paragraphs 10.6 and 10.7 and Tables 6 and 7 for limitations on plastic rooflights.

†   The designation of external roof surfaces is explained in Appendix A. (See Table A5 for notional designations of roof coverings.)

Separation distances do not apply to the boundary between roofs of a pair of semi-detached houses (see para 10.5) and to enclosed/covered walkways. However, see Diagram 11 if the roof passes over the top of a compartment wall.

Openable polycarbonate and PVC rooflights which achieve a Class 1 (National class) or Class C-s3, d2 (European class) rating by test, see paragraph 10.7, may be regarded as having an AA (National class) designation or $B_{ROOF}(t4)$ (European class) classification.

The National classifications do not automatically equate with the equivalent classifications in the European column, therefore products cannot typically assume a European class unless they have been tested accordingly.

● Acceptable.

○ Not acceptable.

1.   Not acceptable on any of the following buildings:
a. Houses in terraces of three or more houses.
b. Any other buildings with a cubic capacity of more than 1500m³.

2.   Acceptable on buildings not listed in Note 1, provided that part of the roof is no more than 3m² in area and is at least 1500mm from any similar part, with the roof between the parts covered with a material of limited combustibility.

Table 6 Class 3 (National class) or Class D-s3,d2 (European class) plastic rooflights: limitations on use and boundary distance

Minimum classification on lower surface [1]	Space which rooflight can serve	Minimum distance from any point on relevant boundary to rooflight with an external designation† of:	
		AD BD CD (National class) or E$_{ROOF}$(t4) (European class) CA CB CC or D$_{ROOF}$(t4) (European class)	DA DB DC DD (National class) or F$_{ROOF}$(t4) (European class)
Class 3 (National class) or Class D-s3, d2 (European class)	a. Balcony, verandah, carport or covered way, which has at least one longer side wholly or permanently open	6m	20m
	b. Detached swimming pool		
	c. Conservatory, garage or outbuilding, with a maximum floor area of 40m²		
	d. Circulation space [2] (except a protected stairway)	6m [3]	20m [3]
	e. Room [2]		

Notes:

†   The designation of external roof surfaces is explained in Appendix A.

    None of the above designations are suitable for protected stairways.

    Polycarbonate and PVC rooflights which achieve a Class 1 (National class) or Class C-s3, d2 (European class) rating by test, see paragraph 10.7, may be regarded as having an AA designation (National class) or B$_{ROOF}$(t4) (European class) classification.

    The National classifications do not automatically equate with the equivalent classifications in the European column, therefore products cannot typically assume a European class unless they have been tested accordingly.

    Where Diagram 11b applies, rooflights should be at least 1.5m from the compartment wall.

    Products may have upper and lower surfaces with different properties if they have double skins or are laminates of different materials; in which case the more onerous distance (from Tables 6 and 7) applies.

1.   See also the guidance to B2.

2.   Single skin rooflight only, in the case of non-thermoplastic material.

3.   The rooflight should also meet the provisions of Diagram 23.

Table 7 TP(a) and TP(b) plastic rooflights: limitations on use and boundary distance

Minimum classification on lower surface [1]	Space which rooflight can serve	Minimum distance from any point on relevant boundary to rooflight with an external surface classification [1] of:	
		TP(a)	TP(b)
1. TP(a) rigid	Any space except a protected stairway	6m [2]	Not applicable
2. TP(b)	a. Balcony, verandah, carport or covered way, which has at least one longer side wholly or permanently open	Not applicable	6m
	b. Detached swimming pool		
	c. Conservatory, garage or outbuilding, with a maximum floor area of 40m²		
	d. Circulation space [3] (except a protected stairway)	Not applicable	6m [4]
	e. Room [3]		

Notes:

    None of the above designations are suitable for protected stairways.

    Polycarbonate and PVC rooflights which achieve a Class 1 (National class) or Class C-s3, d2 (European class) rating by test, see paragraph 10.7, may be regarded as having an AA designation (National class) or B$_{ROOF}$(t4) (European class) classification.

    Where Diagram 11b applies, rooflights should be at least 1.5m from the compartment wall.

    Products may have upper and lower surfaces with different properties if they have double skins or are laminates of different materials; in which case the more onerous distance (from Tables 6 and 7) applies.

    The National classifications do not automatically equate with the equivalent classifications in the European column, therefore products cannot typically assume a European class unless they have been tested accordingly.

1.   See also the guidance to B2.

2.   No limit in the case of any space described in 2a, b & c.

3.   Single skin rooflight only, in the case of non-thermoplastic material.

4.   The rooflight should also meet the provisions of Diagram 23.

The Requirement

This Approved Document deals with the
following Requirement from Part B of Schedule 1
to the Building Regulations 2010 (as amended).

Requirement	Limits on application
Access and facilities for the fire service **B5.** (1) The building shall be designed and constructed so as to provide reasonable facilities to assist firefighters in the protection of life. (2) Reasonable provision shall be made within the site of the building to enable fire appliances to gain access to the building.	

Guidance

Performance

In the Secretary of State's view the Requirements of B5 will be met:

a. if there is sufficient means of external access to enable fire appliances to be brought near to the building for effective use;

b. if there is sufficient means of access into, and within, the building for firefighting personnel to effect search and rescue and fight fire;

c. if the building is provided with sufficient internal fire mains and other facilities to assist firefighters in their tasks; and

d. if the building is provided with adequate means for venting heat and smoke from a fire in a basement.

These access arrangements and facilities are only required in the interests of the health and safety of people in and around the building. The extent to which they are required will depend on the use and size of the building in so far as it affects the health and safety of those people.

Introduction

B5.i   The main factor determining the facilities needed to assist the fire and rescue service is the size of the building. Generally speaking firefighting is carried out within the building.

For dwellinghouses, it is usually only necessary to ensure that the building is sufficiently close to a point accessible to fire and rescue service vehicles (see paragraph 11.2). For very large houses additional measures may be necessary. The guidance given in Approved Document B Volume 2 (Buildings other than dwellinghouses) may be applicable.

If it is proposed to deviate from the general guidance in Section 11 then it would be advisable to seek advice from the Fire and Rescue Service at the earliest opportunity.

Section 11: Vehicle access

Introduction

11.1   For the purposes of this Approved Document, vehicle access to the exterior of a building is needed to enable high reach appliances, such as turntable ladders and hydraulic platforms, to be used and to enable pumping appliances to supply water and equipment for firefighting, search and rescue activities.

Vehicle access routes and hard-standings should meet the criteria described in paragraph 11.4 where they are to be used by fire and rescue service vehicles.

Note: Requirements cannot be made under the Building Regulations for work to be done outside the site of the works shown on the deposited plans, building notice or initial notice. In this connection it may not always be reasonable to upgrade an existing route across a site to a small building such as a single dwellinghouse. The options in such a case, from doing no work to upgrading certain features of the route, e.g. a sharp bend, should be considered by the Building Control Body in consultation with the fire and rescue service.

11.2   There should be vehicle access for a pump appliance to within 45m of all points within the dwellinghouse.

11.3   Every elevation to which vehicle access is provided in accordance with paragraph 11.2 should have a suitable door(s), not less than 750mm wide, giving access to the interior of the building.

Design of access routes and hard-standings

11.4   A vehicle access route may be a road or other route which, including any inspection covers and the like, meets the standards in Table 8 and paragraph 11.5.

11.5   Turning facilities should be provided in any dead end access route that is more than 20m long (see Diagram 24). This can be by a hammerhead or turning circle, designed on the basis of Table 8.

Table 8 Typical fire and rescue service vehicle access route specification

Appliance type	Minimum width of road between kerbs (m)	Minimum width of gateways (m)	Minimum turning circle between kerbs (m)	Minimum turning circle between walls (m)	Minimum clearance height (m)	Minimum carrying capacity (tonnes)
Pump	3.7	3.1	16.8	19.2	3.7	12.5
High reach	3.7	3.1	26.0	29.0	4.0	17.0

Notes:

1.   Fire appliances are not standardised. Some fire and rescue services have appliances of greater weight or different size. In consultation with the Fire and Rescue Authority, the Building Control Body may adopt other dimensions in such circumstances.

2.   Because the weight of high reach appliances is distributed over a number of axles, it is considered that their infrequent use of a carriageway or route designed to 12.5 tonnes should not cause damage. It would therefore be reasonable to design the roadbase to 12.5 tonnes, although structures such as bridges should have the full 17 tonnes capacity.

Diagram 24 Turning facilities

See para 11.5

Fire and rescue service vehicles should not have to reverse more than 20m from the end of an access road

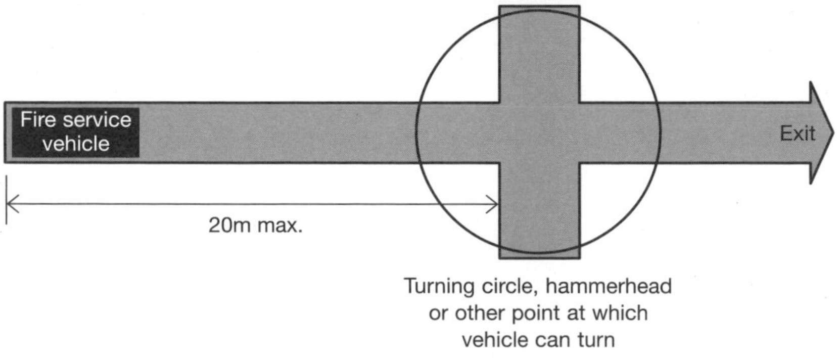

Fire service vehicle

20m max.

Exit

Turning circle, hammerhead or other point at which vehicle can turn

Appendix A: Performance of materials, products and structures

Introduction

1.   Much of the guidance in this document is given in terms of performance in relation to British or European Standards for products or methods of test or design or in terms of European Technical Approvals. In such cases the material, product or structure should:

a.   be in accordance with a specification or design which has been shown by test to be capable of meeting that performance; or

Note: For this purpose, laboratories accredited by the United Kingdom Accreditation Service (UKAS) for conducting the relevant tests would be expected to have the necessary expertise.

b.   have been assessed from test evidence against appropriate standards, or by using relevant design guides, as meeting that performance; or

Note: For this purpose, laboratories accredited by UKAS for conducting the relevant tests and suitably qualified fire safety engineers might be expected to have the necessary expertise.

For materials/products where European standards or approvals are not yet available and for a transition period after they become available, British standards may continue to be used. Any body notified to the UK Government by the Government of another Member State of the European Union as capable of assessing such materials/products against the relevant British Standards, may also be expected to have the necessary expertise. Where European materials/ products standards or approvals are available, any body notified to the European Commission as competent to assess such materials or products against the relevant European standards or technical approval can be considered to have the appropriate expertise.

c.   where tables of notional performance are included in this document, conform with an appropriate specification given in these tables; or

d.   in the case of fire-resisting elements:

   i.   conform with an appropriate specification given in Part II of the Building Research Establishments' Report *Guidelines for the construction of fire-resisting structural elements* (BR 128, BRE 1988); or

   ii.   be designed in accordance with a relevant British Standard or Eurocode.

Note 1: Different forms of construction can present different problems and opportunities for the provision of structural fire protection. Further information on some specific forms of construction can be found in:

• Timber – BRE 454 *Multi-storey timber frame buildings – a design guide* 2003 ISBN: 1 86081 605 3

• Steel – SCI P197 *Designing for structural fire safety: A handbook for architects and engineers* 1999 ISBN: 1 85942 074 5

Note 2: Any test evidence used to substantiate the fire resistance rating of a construction should be carefully checked to ensure that it demonstrates compliance that is adequate and applicable to the intended use. Small differences in detail (such as fixing method, joints, dimensions and the introduction of insulation materials etc.) may significantly affect the rating.

2.   Building Regulations deal with fire safety in buildings as a whole. Thus they are aimed at limiting fire hazard.

The aim of standard fire tests is to measure or assess the response of a material, product, structure or system to one or more aspects of fire behaviour. Standard fire tests cannot normally measure fire hazard. They form only one of a number of factors that need to be taken into account. Other factors are set out in this publication.

Fire resistance

3.   Factors having a bearing on fire resistance, that are considered in this document, are:

a.   fire severity;

b.   building height; and

c.   building occupancy.

4.   The standards of fire resistance given are based on assumptions about the severity of fires and the consequences should an element fail. Fire severity is estimated in very broad terms from the use of the building (its purpose group), on the assumption that the building contents (which constitute the fire load) are similar for buildings in the same use.

A number of factors affect the standard of fire resistance specified. These are:

a.   the amount of combustible material per unit of floor area in various types of building (the fire load density);

b.   the height of the top floor above ground, which affects the ease of escape and of firefighting operations, and the consequences should large scale collapse occur;

c.   occupancy type, which reflects the ease with which the building can be evacuated quickly;

d.   whether there are basements, because the lack of an external wall through which to vent heat and smoke may increase heat build-up and thus affect the duration of a fire, as well as complicating firefighting; and

e. whether the building is of single storey construction (where escape is direct and structural failure is unlikely to precede evacuation).

Because the use of buildings may change, a precise estimate of fire severity based on the fire load due to a particular use may be misleading. Therefore, if a fire engineering approach of this kind is adopted, the likelihood that the fire load may change in the future needs to be considered.

5.   Performance in terms of the fire resistance to be met by elements of structure, doors and other forms of construction is determined by reference to either:

a. (National tests) BS 476 *Fire tests on building materials and structures,* Parts 20-24:1987, i.e. Part 20 *Method for determination of the fire resistance of elements of construction (general principles),* Part 21 *Methods for determination of the fire resistance of loadbearing elements of construction,* Part 22 *Methods for determination of the fire resistance of non-loadbearing elements of construction,* Part 23 *Methods for determination of the contribution of components to the fire resistance of a structure,* and Part 24 *Method for determination of the fire resistance of ventilation ducts* (or to BS 476-8:1972 in respect of items tested or assessed prior to 1 January 1988); or

b. (European tests) Commission Decision 2000/367/EC of 3 May 2000 implementing Council Directive 89/106/EEC as regards the classification of the resistance to fire performance of construction products, construction works and parts thereof.

Note: The latest version of any standard may be used provided that it continues to address the relevant requirements of the Regulations.

All products are classified in accordance with BS EN 13501-2:2007 *Fire classification of construction products and building elements. Classification using data from fire resistance tests, excluding ventilation services (excluding products for use in ventilation systems).*

BS EN 13501-3:2005 *Fire classification of construction products and building elements. Classification using data from fire resistance tests on products and elements used in building service installations: fire resisting ducts and fire dampers (other than smoke control systems).*

BS EN 13501-4:2007, *Fire classification of construction products and building elements, Part 4 – Classification using data from fire resistance tests on smoke control systems.*

The relevant European test methods under BS EN 1364, 1365, 1366 and 1634 are listed in Appendix F.

Table A1 gives the specific requirements for each element in terms of one or more of the following performance criteria:

a. **resistance to collapse** (loadbearing capacity), which applies to loadbearing elements only, denoted R in the European classification of the resistance to fire performance;

b. **resistance to fire penetration** (integrity), denoted E in the European classification of the resistance to fire performance; and

c. **resistance to the transfer of excessive heat** (insulation), denoted I in the European classification of the resistance to fire performance.

Table A2 sets out the minimum periods of fire resistance for elements of structure.

Table A3 sets out criteria appropriate to the suspended ceilings that can be accepted as contributing to the fire resistance of a floor.

Table A4 sets out limitations on the use of uninsulated fire-resisting glazed elements. These limitations do not apply to the use of insulated fire-resisting glazed elements.

Information on tested elements is frequently given in literature available from manufacturers and trade associations.

Information on tests on fire-resisting elements is also given in such publications as:

Association for Specialist Fire Protection Yellow Book – *Fire protection for structural steel in buildings,* 4th edition. See Appendix F.

Roofs

6.   Performance in terms of the resistance of roofs to external fire exposure is determined by reference to either:

a. (National tests) BS 476-3:2004 *External fire exposure roof tests*; or

b. (European tests) Commission Decision 2005/823/EC amending Decision 2001/671/EC *Establishing a classification system for the external fire performance of roofs and roof coverings.*

Constructions are classified within the National system by two letters in the range A-D, with an AA designation being the best. The first letter indicates the time to penetration; the second letter a measure of the spread of flame.

Constructions are classified within the European system as $B_{ROOF}(t4)$, $C_{ROOF}(t4)$, $D_{ROOF}(t4)$, $E_{ROOF}(t4)$ or $F_{ROOF}(t4)$ (with $B_{ROOF}(t4)$ being the highest performance and $F_{ROOF}(t4)$ being the lowest) in accordance with BS EN 13501-5:2005 *Fire classification of construction products and building elements – Classification using data from external fire exposure to roof tests.*

BS EN 13501-5 refers to four separate tests. The suffix (t4) used above indicates that Test 4 is to be used for the purposes of this Approved Document.

Some roof covering products (and/or materials) can be considered to fulfil all of the requirements for the performance characteristic "external fire performance" without the need for testing, subject to any national provisions on the design and execution of works being fulfilled. These roof covering products are listed in Commission Decision 2000/553/EC of 6th September 2000 implementing Council Directive 89/106/EEC as regards the external fire performance of roof coverings.

In some circumstances roofs, or parts of roofs, may need to be fire-resisting, for example if used as an escape route or if the roof performs the function of a floor. Such circumstances are covered in Sections 2, 4 and 6.

Table A5 gives notional designations of some generic roof coverings.

Reaction to fire

7.   Performance in terms of reaction to fire to be met by construction products is determined by Commission Decision 200/147/EC of 8 February 2000 implementing Council Directive 89/106/EEC as regards the classification of the reaction to fire performance of construction products.

Note: The designation of xxxx is used for the year reference for standards that are not yet published. The latest version of any standard may be used provided that it continues to address the relevant requirements of the Regulations.

All products, excluding floorings, are classified as [†]A1, A2, B, C, D, E or F (with class A1 being the highest performance and F being the lowest) in accordance with BS EN 13501-1:2002 *Fire classification of construction products and building elements, Part 1 – Classification using data from reaction to fire tests.*

[†]   The classes of reaction to fire performance of A2, B, C, D and E are accompanied by additional classifications related to the production of smoke (s1, s2, s3) and/or flaming droplets/particles (d0, d1, *d2).*

The relevant European test methods are specified as follows:

- BS EN ISO 1182:2002 *Reaction to fire tests for building products – Non-combustibility test*

- BS EN ISO 1716:2002 *Reaction to fire tests for building products – Determination of the gross calorific value*

- BS EN 13823:2002 *Reaction to fire tests for building products – Building products excluding floorings exposed to the thermal attack by a single burning item*

- BS EN ISO 11925-2:2002 *Reaction to fire tests for building products,* Part 2 – *Ignitability when subjected to direct impingement of a flame.*

- BS EN 13238:2001 *Reaction to fire tests for building products – conditioning procedures and general rules for selection of substrates.*

Non-combustible materials

8.   Non-combustible materials are defined in Table A6 either as listed products, or in terms of performance:

a. (National classes) when tested to BS 476-4:1970 *Fire tests on building materials and structures – Non-combustibility test for materials* or BS 476-11:1982 *Fire tests on building materials and structures – Method for assessing the heat emission from building materials.*

b. (European classes) when classified as class A1 in accordance with BS EN 13501-1:2002 *Fire classification of construction products and building elements. Classification using data from reaction to fire tests* when tested to BS EN ISO 1182:2002 *Reaction to fire tests for building products – Non-combustibility test* **and** BS EN ISO 1716:2002 *Reaction to fire tests for building products – Determination of the gross calorific value.*

Table A6 identifies non-combustible products and materials, and lists circumstances where their use is necessary.

Materials of limited combustibility

9.   Materials of limited combustibility are defined in Table A7:

a. (National classes) by reference to the method specified in BS 476-11:1982;

b. (European classes) in terms of performance when classified as class A2-s3, d2 in accordance with BS EN 13501-1:2002 *Fire classification of construction products and building elements. Classification using data from reaction to fire tests* when tested to BS EN ISO 1182:2002 *Reaction to fire tests for building products – Non-combustibility test* or BS EN ISO 1716:2002 *Reaction to fire tests for building products – Determination of the gross calorific value* **and** BS EN 13823:2002 *Reaction to fire tests for building products – Building products excluding floorings exposed to the thermal attack by a single burning item.*

Table A7 also includes composite products (such as plasterboard) which are considered acceptable, and where these are exposed as linings they should also meet any appropriate flame spread rating.

Internal linings

10. Flame spread over wall or ceiling surfaces is controlled by providing for the lining materials or products to meet given performance levels in tests appropriate to the materials or products involved.

11. Under the National classifications, lining systems which can be effectively tested for 'surface spread of flame' are rated for performance by reference to the method specified in BS 476-7:1997 (or 1987 or 1971) *Fire tests on building materials and structures. Method of test to determine the classification of the surface spread of flame of products* under which materials or products are classified 1, 2, 3 or 4 with Class 1 being the highest.

Under the European classifications, lining systems are classified in accordance with BS EN 13501-1:2002 *Fire classification of construction products and building elements,* Part 1 – *Classification using data from reaction to fire tests.* Materials or products are classified as A1, A2, B, C, D, E or F, with A1 being the highest. When a classification includes 's3, d2', it means that there is no limit set for smoke production and/or flaming droplets/particles.

12. To restrict the use of materials which ignite easily, which have a high rate of heat release and/or which reduce the time to flashover, maximum acceptable 'fire propagation' indices are specified, where the National test methods are being followed. These are determined by reference to the method specified in BS 476-6:1989 or 1981. Index of performance (I) relates to the overall test performance, whereas sub-index (i1) is derived from the first three minutes of test.

13. The highest National product performance classification for lining materials is Class 0. This is achieved if a material or the surface of a composite product is either:

a. composed throughout of materials of limited combustibility; or

b. a Class 1 material which has a fire propagation index (I) of not more than 12 and sub-index (i1) of not more than 6.

Note: Class 0 is not a classification identified in any British Standard test.

14. Composite products defined as materials of limited combustibility (see paragraph 9 and Table A7) should in addition comply with the test requirement appropriate to any surface rating specified in the guidance on requirements B2, B3 and B4.

15. The notional performance ratings of certain widely used generic materials or products are listed in Table A8 in terms of their performance in the traditional lining tests BS 476-6:1989 and BS 476-7:1997 or in accordance with BS EN 13501-1:2002.

16. Results of tests on proprietary materials are frequently given in literature available from manufacturers and trade associations.

Any reference used to substantiate the surface spread of flame rating of a material or product should be carefully checked to ensure that it is suitable, adequate and applicable to the construction to be used. Small differences in detail, such as thickness, substrate, colour, form, fixings, adhesive etc, may significantly affect the rating.

Thermoplastic Materials

17. A thermoplastic material means any synthetic polymeric material which has a softening point below 200°C if tested to BS EN ISO 306:2004 method A120 *Plastics – Thermoplastic materials – Determination of Vicat softening temperature.* Specimens for this test may be fabricated from the original polymer where the thickness of material of the end product is less than 2.5mm.

18. A thermoplastic material in isolation can not be assumed to protect a substrate when used as a lining to a wall or ceiling. The surface rating of both products must therefore meet the required classification. If, however, the thermoplastic material is fully bonded to a non-thermoplastic substrate, then only the surface rating of the composite will need to comply.

19. Concessions are made for thermoplastic materials used for window glazing, rooflights, and lighting diffusers within suspended ceilings, which may not comply with the criteria specified in paragraphs 11 to 16. They are described in the guidance on requirements B2 and B4.

20. For the purposes of the requirements B2 and B4 thermoplastic materials should either be used according to their classification 0-3, under the BS 476-6:1989 and BS 476-7:1997 tests as described in paragraphs 11 to 16, (if they have such a rating), or they may be classified TP(a) rigid, TP(a) flexible, or TP(b) according to the following methods:

TP(a) rigid:

i. Rigid solid pvc sheet;

ii. Solid (as distinct from double- or multiple-skin) polycarbonate sheet at least 3mm thick;

iii. Multi-skinned rigid sheet made from unplasticised pvc or polycarbonate which has a Class 1 rating when tested to BS 476-7:1997 or 1971 or 1987; and

iv. Any other rigid thermoplastic product, a specimen of which (at the thickness of the product as put on the market), when tested to BS 2782:1970 as amended in 1974: Method 508A *Rate of burning (Laboratory method),* performs so that the test flame extinguishes before the first mark and the duration of flaming or afterglow does not exceed five seconds following removal of the burner.

TP(a) flexible:

Flexible products not more than 1mm thick which comply with the Type C requirements of BS 5867-2:1980 *Specification for fabrics for curtains and drapes – Flammability requirements* when tested to BS 5438:1989 *Methods of test for flammability of textile fabrics when subjected to a small igniting flame applied to the face or bottom edge of vertically oriented specimens,* Test 2, with the flame applied to the surface of the specimens for 5, 15, 20 and 30 seconds respectively, but excluding the cleansing procedure; and

TP(b):

i. Rigid solid polycarbonate sheet products less than 3mm thick, or multiple-skin polycarbonate sheet products which do not qualify as TP(a) by test; or

ii. Other products which, when a specimen of the material between 1.5 and 3mm thick is tested in accordance with BS 2782:1970, as amended in 1974: Method 508A, has a rate of burning which does not exceed 50mm/minute.

Note: If it is not possible to cut or machine a 3mm-thick specimen from the product then a 3mm test specimen can be moulded from the same material as that used for the manufacture of the product.

Note: Currently, no new guidance is possible on the assessment or classification of thermoplastic materials under the European system since there is no generally accepted European test procedure and supporting comparative data.

Fire test methods

21.   A guide to the various test methods in BS 476 and BS 2782 is given in PD 6520 *Guide to fire test methods for building materials and elements of construction* (available from the British Standards Institution).

A guide to the development and presentation of fire tests and their use in hazard assessment is given in BS 6336:1998 *Guide to development and presentation of fire tests and their use in hazard assessment.*

Table A1 Specific provisions of test for fire resistance of elements of structure etc

Part of building	Minimum provisions when tested to the relevant part of BS 476 [1] (minutes)			Minimum provisions when tested to the relevant European standard (minutes) [9]	Method of exposure
	Loadbearing capacity [2]	Integrity	Insulation		
1. **Structural** frame, beam or column.	See Table A2	Not applicable	Not applicable	R see Table A2	Exposed faces
2. **Loadbearing wall** (which is not also a wall described in any of the following items).	See Table A2	Not applicable	Not applicable	R see Table A2	Each side separately
3. **Floor** [3]					
a. In upper storey of 2-storey dwellinghouse (but not over garage or basement);	30	15	15	R 30 and REI 15	From underside
b. Any other floor – including compartment floors.	See Table A2	See Table A2	See Table A2	REI see Table A2	From underside
4. **Roof** any part forming an escape route;	30	30	30	REI 30	From underside [4]
5. **External walls**					
a. any part less than 1000mm from any point on the relevant boundary;	See Table A2	See Table A2	See Table A2	REI see Table A2	Each side separately
b. any part 1000mm or more from the relevant boundary [5];	See Table A2	See Table A2	15	RE see Table A2 and REI 15	From inside the building
c. any part adjacent to an external escape route (see paragraph 2.10 and 2.15 and Diagram 7).	30	30	No provision [6][7]	RE 30	From inside the building
6. **Compartment walls** (other than in item 8)	See Table A2	See Table A2	See Table A2	REI see Table A2	Each side separately

Table A1 **continued**

Part of building	Minimum provisions when tested to the relevant part of BS 476 [1] (minutes)			Minimum provisions when tested to the relevant European standard (minutes) [9]	Method of exposure
	Loadbearing capacity [2]	Integrity	Insulation		
7. **Enclosure** (which does not form part of a compartment wall or a protected shaft) to a: a. protected stairway;	30	30	30 [8]	REI 30 [8]	Each side separately
b. lift shaft.	30	30	30	REI 30	Each side separately
8. **Wall or floor** separating an attached or integral garage from a dwellinghouse	30	30	30 [8]	REI 30 [8]	From garage side
9. **Fire-resisting construction:** in dwellinghouses not described elsewhere	30	30	30 [8]	REI 30 [8]	
10. **Cavity barrier**	Not applicable	30	15	E 30 and EI 15	Each side separately
11. **Ceiling** described in paragraph 2.14, Diagram 6	Not applicable	30	30	EI 30	From underside
12. **Duct** described in paragraph 6.8e	Not applicable	30	No provision	E 30	From outside
13. **Casing** around a drainage system described in paragraph 7.8, Diagram 15	Not applicable	30	No provision	E 30	From outside
14. **Flue walls** described in paragraph 7.11, Diagram 16	Not applicable	Half the period specified in Table A2 for the compartment wall/floor	Half the period specified in Table A2 for the compartment wall/floor	EI half the period specified in Table A2 for the compartment wall/floor	From outside
15. **Construction** described in Note (a) to paragraph 10.9	Not applicable	30	30	EI 30	From underside
16. **Fire doors**		See Table B1		See Table B1	

Notes:

1. Part 21 for loadbearing elements, Part 22 for non-loadbearing elements, Part 23 for fire-protecting suspended ceilings, and Part 24 for ventilation ducts. BS 476-8 results are acceptable for items tested or assessed before 1 January 1988.

2. Applies to loadbearing elements only (see B3.ii and Appendix E).

3. Guidance on increasing the fire resistance of existing timber floors is given in BRE Digest 208 Increasing the fire resistance of existing timber floors (BRE 1988).

4. A suspended ceiling should only be relied on to contribute to the fire resistance of the floor if the ceiling meets the appropriate provisions given in Table A3.

5. The guidance in Section 9 allows such walls to contain areas which need not be fire-resisting (unprotected areas).

6. Unless needed as part of a wall in item 5a or 5b.

7. Except for any limitations on glazed elements given in Table A4.

8. See Table A4 for permitted extent of uninsulated glazed elements.

9. The National classifications do not automatically equate with the equivalent classifications in the European column, therefore products cannot typically assume a European class unless they have been tested accordingly.

   'R' is the European classification of the resistance to fire performance in respect of loadbearing capacity; 'E' is the European classification of the resistance to fire performance in respect of integrity; and 'I' is the European classification of the resistance to fire performance in respect of insulation.

Table A2 Minimum periods of fire resistance for dwellinghouses

Minimum periods (minutes) for elements of structure in a:

Basement storey [1] including floor over	Ground or upper storey	
	Height (m) of top floor above ground	
	Not more than 5	More than 5
30 [2]	30 [2]	60 [3]

Notes:

Modifications referred to in Table A2:

1. The floor over a basement (or if there is more than one basement, the floor over the topmost basement) should meet the provisions for the ground and upper storeys if that period is higher.

2. Increased to a minimum of 60 minutes for compartment walls separating buildings.

3. 30 minutes in the case of three storey dwellinghouses, increased to 60 minutes minimum for compartment walls separating buildings.

4. Refer to Table A1 for the specific provisions of test.

Application of the fire resistance standards in table A2:

a. Where one element of structure supports or carries or gives stability to another, the fire resistance of the supporting element should be no less than the minimum period of fire resistance for the other element (whether that other element is loadbearing or not).

There are circumstances where it may be reasonable to vary this principle, for example:

  i. where the supporting structure is in the open air, and is not likely to be affected by the fire in the building; or

  ii. where the supporting structure is in a different compartment, with a fire-separating element (which has the higher standard of fire resistance) between the supporting and the separated structure; or

  iii. where a plant room on the roof needs a higher fire resistance than the elements of structure supporting it.

b. Where an element of structure forms part of more than one building or compartment, that element should be constructed to the standard of the greater of the relevant provisions.

c. Although most elements of structure in a single storey building may not need fire resistance (see the guidance on requirement B3, paragraph 4.4(a)), fire resistance will be needed if the element:

  i. is part of (or supports) an external wall and there is provision in the guidance on requirement B4 to limit the extent of openings and other unprotected areas in the wall; or

  ii. is part of (or supports) a compartment wall, including a wall common to two or more buildings, or a wall between a dwellinghouse and an attached or integral garage; or

  iii. supports a gallery.

For the purposes of this paragraph, the ground storey of a building which has one or more basement storeys and no upper storeys, may be considered as a single-storey building. The fire resistance of the basement storeys should be that appropriate to basements.

Table A3 Limitations on fire-protecting suspended ceilings (see Table A1, Note 4)

Height of building or separated part (m)	Type of floor	Provision for fire resistance of floor (minutes)	Description of suspended ceiling
Less than 18	Not compartment	60 or less	Type W, X, Y or Z
	Compartment	less than 60	
		60	Type X, Y or Z
18 or more	any	60 or less	Type Y or Z
No limit	any	More than 60	Type Z

Notes:

1. Ceiling type and description (the change from Types A-D to Types W-Z is to avoid confusion with Classes A-D (European)):

    W. Surface of ceiling exposed to the cavity should be Class 0 or Class 1 (National) or Class C-s3, d2 or better (European).

    X. Surface of ceiling exposed to the cavity should be Class 0 (National) or Class B-s3, d2 or better (European).

    Y. Surface of ceiling exposed to the cavity should be Class 0 (National) or Class B-s3, d2 or better (European). Ceiling should not contain easily openable access panels.

    Z. Ceiling should be of a material of limited combustibility (National) or of Class A2-s3, d2 or better (European) and not contain easily openable access panels. Any insulation above the ceiling should be of a material of limited combustibility (National) or Class A2-s3, d2 or better (European).

2. Any access panels provided in fire protecting suspended ceilings of type Y or Z should be secured in position by releasing devices or screw fixings, and they should be shown to have been tested in the ceiling assembly in which they are incorporated.

3. The National classifications do not automatically equate with the equivalent European classifications, therefore products cannot typically assume a European class unless they have been tested accordingly.

    When a classification includes 's3, d2', this means that there is no limit set for smoke production and/or flaming droplets/particles.

Table A4 Limitations on the use of uninsulated glazed elements on escape routes (These limitations do not apply to glazed elements which satisfy the relevant insulation criterion, see Table A1)

Position of glazed element	Maximum total glazed area in parts of a building with access to:			
	A single stairway		More than one stairway	
	Walls	Door leaf	Walls	Door leaf
1. Within the enclosures of a protected stairway, or within fire-resisting separation shown in Section 2 Diagram 2;	Unlimited above 1100mm from floor or pitch of the stair	Unlimited	Unlimited above 1100mm from floor or pitch of the stair	Unlimited
2. Within fire-resisting separation: (i) shown in Section 2 Diagram 4; or (ii) described in para 2.13b.	Unlimited above 100mm from floor	Unlimited above 100mm from floor	Unlimited above 100mm from floor	Unlimited above 100mm from floor
3. Existing window between an attached/integral garage and the dwellinghouse.	Unlimited	Not applicable	Unlimited	Not applicable
4. Adjacent to an external escape stair (see para 2.15 and Diagram 7) or roof escape (see para 2.10).	Unlimited	Unlimited	Unlimited	Unlimited

Notes:

1. The 100mm limit is intended to reduce the risk of fire spread from a floor covering.

2. Fire-resisting glass should be marked with the manufacturer and product name.

3. Good guidance can be found in A guide to best practice in the specification and use of fire-resistant glazed systems published by the Glass and Glazing Federation.

Table A5 **Notional designations of roof coverings**

Part i: Pitched roofs covered with slates or tiles

Covering material	Supporting structure	Designation
1. Natural slates 2. Fibre reinforced cement slates 3. Clay tiles 4. Concrete tiles	Timber rafters with or without underfelt, sarking, boarding, woodwool slabs, compressed straw slabs, plywood, wood chipboard, or fibre insulating board	AA (National class) or B_{ROOF}(t4) (European class)

Note: Although the Table does not include guidance for roofs covered with bitumen felt, it should be noted that there is a wide range of materials on the market and information on specific products is readily available from manufacturers.

Part ii: Pitched roofs covered with self-supporting sheet

Roof covering material	Construction	Supporting structure	Designation
1. Profiled sheet of galvanised steel, aluminium, fibre reinforced cement, or pre-painted (coil coated) steel or aluminium with a pvc or pvf2 coating	Single skin without underlay, or with underlay or plasterboard, fibre insulating board, or woodwool slab	Structure of timber, steel or concrete	AA (National class) or B_{ROOF}(t4) (European class)
2. Profiled sheet of galvanised steel, aluminium, fibre reinforced cement, or pre-painted (coil coated) steel or aluminium with a pvc or pvf2 coating	Double skin without interlayer, or with interlayer of resin bonded glass fibre, mineral wool slab, polystyrene, or polyurethane	Structure of timber, steel or concrete	AA (National class) or B_{ROOF}(t4) (European class)

Part iii. Flat roofs covered with bitumen felt

A flat roof comprising bitumen felt should (irrespective of the felt specification) be deemed to be of designation AA (National class) or B_{ROOF}(t4) (European class) if the felt is laid on a deck constructed of 6mm plywood, 12.5mm wood chipboard, 16mm (finished) plain edged timber boarding, compressed straw slab, screeded wood wool slab, profiled fibre reinforced cement or steel deck (single or double skin) with or without fibre insulating board overlay, profiled aluminium deck (single or double skin) with or without fibre insulating board overlay, or concrete or clay pot slab (insitu or pre cast), and has a surface finish of:

a. bitumen-bedded stone chippings covering the whole surface to a depth of at least 12.5mm;

b. bitumen-bedded tiles of a non-combustible material;

c. sand and cement screed; or

d. macadam.

Part iv. Pitched or flat roofs covered with fully supported material

Covering material	Supporting structure	Designation
1. Aluminium sheet 2. Copper sheet 3. Zinc sheet 4. Lead sheet 5. Mastic asphalt	timber joists and: tongued and grooved boarding, or plain edged boarding	AA* (National class) or B_{ROOF}(t4) (European class)
6. Vitreous enamelled steel 7. Lead/tin alloy coated steel sheet 8. Zinc/aluminium alloy coated steel sheet	steel or timber joists with deck of:. woodwool slabs, compressed straw slab, wood chipboard, fibre insulating board, or 9.5mm plywood	AA (National class) or B_{ROOF}(t4) (European class)
9. Pre-painted (coil coated) steel sheet including liquid-applied pvc coatings	concrete or clay pot slab (insitu or pre-cast) or non-combustible deck of steel, aluminium, or fibre cement (with or without insulation)	AA (National class) or B_{ROOF}(t4) (European class)

Notes:

* Lead sheet supported by timber joists and plain edged boarding should be regarded as having a BA designation and is deemed to be designated class C_{ROOF}(t4) (European class).

The National classifications do not automatically equate with the equivalent classifications in the European column, therefore products cannot typically assume a European class unless they have been tested accordingly.

Table A6 Use and definitions of non-combustible materials

References in AD B guidance to situations where such materials should be used	Definitions of non-combustible materials	
	National class	**European class**
1. Pipes meeting the provisions in the guidance to B3, Table 3. 2. Flue walls meeting the provisions in the guidance to B3, Diagram 16.	a. Any material which when tested to BS 476-11:1982 does not flame nor cause any rise in temperature on either the centre (specimen) or furnace thermocouples b. Totally inorganic materials such as concrete, fired clay, ceramics, metals, plaster and masonry containing not more than 1% by weight or volume of organic material. (Use in buildings of combustible metals such as magnesium/aluminium alloys should be assessed in each individual case). c. Concrete bricks or blocks meeting BS EN 771-3:2003 d. Products classified as non-combustible under BS 476-4:1970	a. Any material classified as class A1 in accordance with BS EN 13501-1:2002 *Fire classification of construction products and building elements. Classification using data from reaction to fire tests.* b. Products made from one or more of the materials considered as Class A1 without the need for testing as defined in Commission Decision 2003/424/EC of 6th June 2003 amending Decision 96/603/EC establishing the list of products belonging to Classes A1 "No contribution to fire" provided for in the Decision 94/611/EC implementing Article 20 of the Council Directive 89/106/EEC on construction products. None of the materials shall contain more than 1% by weight or volume (whichever is the more onerous) of homogeneously distributed organic material.

Note:

The National classifications do not automatically equate with the equivalent classifications in the European column, therefore products cannot typically assume a European class unless they have been tested accordingly.

Table A7 Use and definitions of materials of limited combustibility

References in AD B guidance to situations where such materials should be used	Definitions of materials of limited combustibility	
	National class	**European class**
1. Reinforcement/support for fire-stopping referred to in the guidance to B3, see 7.13. 2. Roof coverings meeting provisions: a. in the guidance to B4, Table 5 or b. in the guidance to B4, Diagram 23. 3. Class 0 materials meeting the provisions in Appendix A, paragraph 13(a). 4. Ceiling tiles or panels of any fire-protecting suspended ceiling (Type Z) in Table A3.	a. Any non-combustible material listed in Table A6. b. Any material of density 300/kg/m³ or more, which when tested to BS 476-11:1982, does not flame and the rise in temperature on the furnace thermocouple is not more than 20°C. c. Any material with a non-combustible core at least 8mm thick having combustible facings (on one or both sides) not more than 0.5mm thick. (Where a flame spread rating is specified, these materials must also meet the appropriate test requirements).	a. Any material listed in Table A6. b. Any material/product classified as Class A2-s3, d2 or better in accordance with BS EN 13501-1:2002 *Fire classification of construction products and building elements. Classification using data from reaction to fire tests.*
5. Insulation above any fire-protecting suspended ceiling (Type Z) in Table A3.	Any of the materials (a), (b) or (c) above, or: d. Any material of density less than 300kg/m³, which when tested to BS 476-11:1982, does not flame for more than 10 seconds and the rise in temperature on the centre (specimen) thermocouple is not more than 35°C and on the furnace thermocouple is not more than 25°C.	Any of the materials/products (a) or (b) above.

Note:

1. The National classifications do not automatically equate with the equivalent classifications in the European column, therefore products cannot typically assume a European class unless they have been tested accordingly.

2. When a classification includes "s3, d2", this means that there is no limit set for smoke production and/or flaming droplets/particles.

Table A8 **Typical performance ratings of some generic materials and products**

Rating	Material or product
Class 0 (National)	1. Any non-combustible material or material of limited combustibility. (composite products listed in Table A7 must meet test requirements given in Appendix A, paragraph 13(b)).
	2. Brickwork, blockwork, concrete and ceramic tiles.
	3. Plasterboard (painted or not with a PVC facing not more than 0.5mm thick) with or without an air gap or fibrous or cellular insulating material behind.
	4. Woodwool cement slabs.
	5. Mineral fibre tiles or sheets with cement or resin binding.
Class 3 (National)	6. Timber or plywood with a density more than 400kg/m^3, painted or unpainted.
	7. Wood particle board or hardboard, either untreated or painted.
	8. Standard glass reinforced polyesters.
Class A1 (European)	9. Any material that achieves this class or is defined as 'classified without further test' in a published Commission Decision.
Class A2-s3, d2 (European)	10. Any material that achieves this class or is defined as 'classified without further test' in a published Commission Decision.
Class B-s3, d2 (European)	11. Any material that achieves this class or is defined as 'classified without further test' in a published Commission Decision.
Class C-s3, d2 (European)	12. Any material that achieves this class or is defined as 'classified without further test' in a published Commission Decision.
Class D-s3, d2 (European)	13. Any material that achieves this class or is defined as 'classified without further test' in a published Commission Decision.

Notes (National):

1. Materials and products listed under Class 0 also meet Class 1.

2. Timber products listed under Class 3 can be brought up to Class 1 with appropriate proprietary treatments.

3. The following materials and products may achieve the ratings listed below. However, as the properties of different products with the same generic description vary, the ratings of these materials/products should be substantiated by test evidence.

   Class 0 – aluminium faced fibre insulating board, flame retardant decorative laminates on a calcium silicate board, thick polycarbonate sheet, phenolic sheet and UPVC.

   Class 1 – phenolic or melamine laminates on a calcium silicate substrate and flame-retardant decorative laminates on a combustible substrate.

Notes (European):

For the purposes of the Building Regulations:

1. Materials and products listed under Class A1 also meet Classes A2-s3, d2, B-s3, d2, C-s3, d2 and D-s3, d2.

2. Materials and products listed under Class A2-s3, d2 also meet Classes B-s3, d2, C-s3, d2 and D-s3, d2.

3. Materials and products listed under Class B-s3, d2 also meet Classes C-s3, d2 and D-s3, d2.

4. Materials and products listed under Class C-s3, d2 also meet Class D-s3, d2.

5. The performance of timber products listed under Class D-s3, d2 can be improved with appropriate proprietary treatments.

6. Materials covered by the CWFT process (classification without further testing) can be found by accessing the European Commission's website via the link on the CLG website www.communities.gov.uk

7. The national classifications do not automatically equate with the equivalent classifications in the European column, therefore products cannot typically assume a European class unless they have been tested accordingly.

8. When a classification includes 's3, d2', this means that there is no limit set for smoke production and/or flaming droplets/particles.

Appendix B: Fire doors

1. All fire doors should have the appropriate performance given in Table B1 either:

a. by their performance under test to BS 476-22 *Fire tests on building materials and structures. Methods for determination of the fire resistance of non-loadbearing elements of construction*, in terms of integrity for a period of minutes, e.g. FD30. A suffix (S) is added for doors where restricted smoke leakage at ambient temperatures is needed; or

b. as determined with reference to Commission Decision 2000/367/EC of 3 May 2000 implementing Council Directive 89/106/EEC as regards the classification of the resistance to fire performance of construction products, construction works and parts thereof. All fire doors should be classified in accordance with BS EN 13501-2:2003 *Fire classification of construction products and building elements. Classification using data from fire resistance tests (excluding products for use in ventilation systems)*. They are tested to the relevant European method from the following:

BS EN 1634-1:2008 *Fire resistance and smoke control tests for door and shutter assemblies, openable windows and elements of building hardware. Fire resistance tests for doors, shutters and openable windows;*

BS EN 1634-2:2008 *Fire resistance and smoke control tests for door and shutter assemblies, openable windows and elements of building hardware. Fire resistance characterisation test for elements of building hardware;*

BS EN 1634-3:2004 *Fire resistance and smoke control tests for door and shutter assemblies, openable windows and elements of building hardware. Smoke control test for door and shutter assemblies.*

The performance requirement is in terms of integrity (E) for a period of minutes. An additional classification of S_a is used for all doors where restricted smoke leakage at ambient temperatures is needed.

The requirement (in either case) is for test exposure from each side of the door separately.

Any test evidence used to substantiate the fire resistance rating of a door or shutter should be carefully checked to ensure that it adequately demonstrates compliance and is applicable to the adequately **complete installed assembly**. Small differences in detail (such as glazing apertures, intumescent strips, door frames and ironmongery etc.) may significantly affect the rating.

Note 1: The latest version of any standard may be used provided that it continues to address the relevant requirements of the Regulations.

Note 2: Until such time that the relevant harmonised product standards are published, for the purposes of meeting the Building Regulations, products tested in accordance with BS EN 1634-1 (with or without pre-fire test mechanical conditioning) will be deemed to have satisfied the provisions provided that they achieve the minimum fire resistance in terms of integrity, as detailed in Table B1.

2. Fire doors serving an attached or integral garage should be fitted with a self-closing device.

3. Unless shown to be satisfactory when tested as part of a fire door assembly, the essential components of any hinge on which a fire door is hung should be made entirely from materials having a melting point of at least 800°C.

4. Tables A1 and A2 set out the minimum periods of fire resistance for the elements of structure to which performance of some doors is linked. Table A4 sets out limitations on the use of uninsulated glazing in fire doors.

5. BS 8214:1990 gives recommendations for the specification, design, construction, installation and maintenance of fire doors constructed with non-metallic door leaves.

Guidance on timber fire-resisting doorsets, in relation to the new European test standard, may be found in *Timber fire-resisting doorsets: maintaining performance under the new European test standard* published by TRADA (Timber Research and Development Association).

Guidance for metal doors is given in *Code of practice for fire-resisting metal doorsets* published by the DSMA (Door and Shutter Manufacturers' Association) in 1999.

6. Hardware used on fire doors can significantly affect performance in fire. Notwithstanding the guidance in this Approved Document guidance is available in *Hardware for fire and escape doors* published by the Builders' Hardware Industry Federation.

Table B1 Provision for fire doors

Position of door	Minimum fire resistance of door in terms of integrity (minutes) when tested to BS 476-22:1987 [1]	Minimum fire resistance of door in terms of integrity (minutes) when tested to the relevant European standard [3]
1. Any door:		
a. within a cavity barrier	FD 30	E30
b. between a dwellinghouse and a garage	FD 30s [2]	E30Sa [2]
c. forming part of the enclosures to a protected stairway in a single family dwellinghouse	FD 20	E20
d. within any other fire-resisting construction in a dwellinghouse not described elsewhere in this table	FD 20	E20

Notes:

1. To BS 476-22:1987 (or BS 476-8:1972 subject to paragraph 5 in Appendix A).

2. Unless pressurization techniques complying with BS EN 12101-6:2005 *Code of practice for smoke control using pressure differentials* are used, these doors should also either:

   (a) have a leakage rate not exceeding 3m³/m/hour (head and jambs only) when tested at 25 Pa under BS 476 *Fire tests on building materials and structures*, Section 31.1 *Methods for measuring smoke penetration through doorsets and shutter assemblies, Method of measurement under ambient temperature conditions*; or

   (b) meet the additional classification requirement of Sa when tested to BS EN 1634-3:2001 *Fire resistance tests for door and shutter assemblies*, Part 3 – *Smoke control doors*.

3. The National classifications do not automatically equate with the equivalent classifications in the European column, therefore products cannot typically assume a European class unless they have been tested accordingly.

B

Appendix C: Methods of measurement

1. Some form of measurement is an integral part of many of the provisions in this document. Diagram C1 shows how the height of the top storey should be measured.

Diagram C1	**Height of top storey in building**

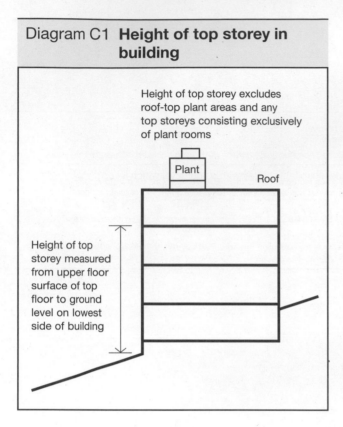

Height of top storey excludes roof-top plant areas and any top storeys consisting exclusively of plant rooms

Plant

Roof

Height of top storey measured from upper floor surface of top floor to ground level on lowest side of building

Appendix D: Purpose groups

1. Many of the provisions in this document are related to the use of the building. The use classifications are termed purpose groups and represent different levels of hazard. They can apply to a whole building, or (where a building is compartmented) to a compartment in the building, and the relevant purpose group should be taken from the main use of the building or compartment.

2. Table D1 sets out the purpose group classification.

Note: This is only of relevance to this Approved Document.

Table D1 Classification of Purpose Groups

Title	Group	Purpose for which the building or compartment of a building is intended to be used
Residential (dwellings)	1(a)*	Flat.
	1(b)†	Dwellinghouse which contains a habitable storey with a floor level which is more than 4.5m above ground level.
	1(c)†	Dwellinghouse which does not contain a habitable storey with a floor level which is more than 4.5m above ground level.
Residential (Institutional)	2(a)	Hospital, home, school or other similar establishment used as living accommodation for, or for the treatment, care or maintenance of persons suffering from disabilities due to illness or old age or other physical or mental incapacity, or under the age of 5 years, or place of lawful detention, where such persons sleep on the premises.
(Other)	2(b)	Hotel, boarding house, residential college, hall of residence, hostel, and any other residential purpose not described above.
Office	3	Offices or premises used for the purpose of administration, clerical work (including writing, book keeping, sorting papers, filing, typing, duplicating, machine calculating, drawing and the editorial preparation of matter for publication, police and fire and rescue service work), handling money (including banking and building society work), and communications (including postal, telegraph and radio communications) or radio, television, film, audio or video recording, or performance (not open to the public) and their control.
Shop and commercial	4	Shops or premises used for a retail trade or business (including the sale to members of the public of food or drink for immediate consumption and retail by auction, self-selection and over-the-counter wholesale trading, the business of lending books or periodicals for gain and the business of a barber or hairdresser and the rental of storage space to the public) and premises to which the public is invited to deliver or collect goods in connection with their hire repair or other treatment, or (except in the case of repair of motor vehicles) where they themselves may carry out such repairs or other treatments.
Assembly and recreation	5	Place of assembly, entertainment or recreation; including bingo halls, broadcasting, recording and film studios open to the public, casinos, dance halls; entertainment, conference, exhibition and leisure centres; funfairs and amusement arcades; museums and art galleries; non-residential clubs, theatres, cinemas and concert halls; educational establishments, dancing schools, gymnasia, swimming pool buildings, riding schools, skating rinks, sports pavilions, sports stadia; law courts; churches and other buildings of worship, crematoria; libraries open to the public, non-residential day centres, clinics, health centres and surgeries; passenger stations and termini for air, rail, road or sea travel; public toilets; zoos and menageries.
Industrial	6	Factories and other premises used for manufacturing, altering, repairing, cleaning, washing, breaking-up, adapting or processing any article; generating power or slaughtering livestock.
Storage and other non-residential+	7(a)	Place for the storage or deposit of goods or materials (other than described under 7(b)) and any building not within any of the Purpose Groups 1 to 6.
	7(b)	Car parks designed to admit and accommodate only cars, motorcycles and passenger or light goods vehicles weighing no more than 2500kg gross.

Notes:

This table only applies to Part B.

* Includes live/work units that meet the provisions of paragraph 2.52 of Volume 2.

† Includes any surgeries, consulting rooms, offices or other accommodation, not exceeding 50m² in total, forming part of a dwelling and used by an occupant of the dwelling in a professional or business capacity.

+ A detached garage not more than 40m² in area is included in Purpose Group 1(c); as is a detached open carport of not more than 40m², or a detached building which consists of a garage and open carport where neither the garage nor open carport exceeds 40m² in area.

Appendix E: Definitions

Note: Except for the items marked * (which are from the Building Regulations), these definitions apply only to Part B.

Access room A room through which the only escape route from an inner room passes.

Accommodation stair A stair, additional to that or those required for escape purposes, provided for the convenience of occupants.

Alternative escape routes Escape routes sufficiently separated by either direction and space, or by fire-resisting construction, to ensure that one is still available should the other be affected by fire.

Note: A second stair, balcony or flat roof which enables a person to reach a place free from danger from fire, is considered an alternative escape route for the purposes of a dwellinghouse.

Alternative exit One of two or more exits, each of which is separate from the other.

Appliance ventilation duct A duct provided to convey combustion air to a gas appliance.

Automatic release mechanism A device which will allow a door held open by it to close automatically in the event of each or any one of the following:

a. detection of smoke by automatic apparatus suitable in nature, quality and location;

b. operation of a hand-operated switch fitted in a suitable position;

c. failure of electricity supply to the device, apparatus or switch;

d. operation of the fire alarm system if any.

Basement storey A storey with a floor which at some point is more than 1200mm below the highest level of ground adjacent to the outside walls.

Boundary The boundary of the land belonging to the building, or where the land abuts a road, railway, canal or river, the centre line of that road, railway, canal or river (See Diagram 17.)

* Building Any permanent or temporary building but not any other kind of structure or erection. A reference to a building includes a reference to part of a building.

Building Control Body A term used to include both Local Authority Building Control and Approved Inspectors.

Cavity barrier A construction, other than a smoke curtain, provided to close a concealed space against penetration of smoke or flame, or provided to restrict the movement of smoke or flame within such a space.

Ceiling A part of a building which encloses and is exposed overhead in a room, protected shaft or circulation space. (The soffit of a rooflight is included as part of the surface of the ceiling, but not the frame. An upstand below a rooflight would be considered as a wall.)

Circulation space A space (including a protected stairway) mainly used as a means of access between a room and an exit from the building or compartment.

Class 0 A product performance classification for wall and ceiling linings. The relevant test criteria are set out in Appendix A, paragraph 13.

Compartment (fire) A building or part of a building, comprising one or more rooms, spaces or storeys, constructed to prevent the spread of fire to or from another part of the same building, or an adjoining building. (A roof space above the top storey of a compartment is included in that compartment.) (See also 'Separated part'.)

Compartment wall or floor A fire-resisting wall/floor used in the separation of one fire compartment from another. (Constructional provisions are given in Section 5.)

Concealed space or cavity A space enclosed by elements of a building (including a suspended ceiling) or contained within an element, but not a room, cupboard, circulation space, protected shaft or space within a flue, chute, duct, pipe or conduit.

Dead end Area from which escape is possible in one direction only.

Direct distance The shortest distance from any point within the floor area, measured within the external enclosures of the building, to the nearest storey exit ignoring walls, partitions and fittings, other than the enclosing walls/partitions to protected stairways.

Dwellinghouse A unit of residential accommodation occupied (whether or not as a sole or main residence):

a. by a single person or by people living together as a family

b. by not more than six residents living together as a single household, including a household where care is provided for residents. (See also paragraphs 0.22 and 0.23.)

* Dwellinghouse does not include a flat or a building containing a flat.

Element of structure:

a. a member forming part of the structural frame of a building or any other beam or column;

b. a loadbearing wall or loadbearing part of a wall;

c. a floor;

d. a gallery (but not a loading gallery, fly gallery, stage grid, lighting bridge, or any gallery provided for similar purposes or for maintenance and repair);

e. an external wall;

f. a compartment wall (including a wall common to two or more buildings). (However, see the guidance to B3, paragraph 4.4, for exclusions from the provisions for elements of structure.)

Escape lighting That part of the emergency lighting which is provided to ensure that the escape route is illuminated at all material times.

Escape route Route forming that part of the means of escape from any point in a building to a final exit.

European Technical Approval A favourable technical assessment of the fitness for use of a construction product for an intended use, issued for the purposes of the Construction Products Directive by a body authorised by a Member State to issue European Technical Approvals for those purposes and notified by that Member State to the European Commission.

European Technical Approvals issuing body A body notified under Article 10 of the Construction Products Directive. The details of these institutions are published in the 'C' series of the *Official Journal of the European Communities*.

Evacuation lift A lift that may be used for the evacuation of people in a fire.

Exit passageway A protected passageway connecting a protected stairway to a final exit (exit passageways should be protected to the same standard as the stairway that they serve).

External wall (or side of a building) Includes a part of a roof pitched at an angle of more than 70° to the horizontal, if that part of the roof adjoins a space within the building to which persons have access (but not access only for repair or maintenance).

Final exit The termination of an escape route from a building giving direct access to a street, passageway, walkway or open space, and sited to ensure the rapid dispersal of persons from the vicinity of a building so that they are no longer in danger from fire and/or smoke.

Note: Windows are not acceptable as final exits.

Fire door A door or shutter, provided for the passage of persons, air or objects, which together with its frame and furniture as installed in a building, is intended (when closed) to resist the passage of fire and/or gaseous products of combustion, and is capable of meeting specified performance criteria to those ends. (It may have one or more leaves, and the term includes a cover or other form of protection to an opening in a fire-resisting wall or floor, or in a structure surrounding a protected shaft.)

Fire-resisting (fire resistance) The ability of a component or construction of a building to satisfy, for a stated period of time, some or all of the appropriate criteria specified in the relevant part of BS 476.

Fire-separating element A compartment wall, compartment floor, cavity barrier and construction enclosing a protected escape route and/or a place of special fire hazard.

Fire stop A seal provided to close an imperfection of fit or design tolerance between elements or components, to restrict the passage of fire and smoke.

* **Flat** A separate and self-contained premises constructed or adapted for use for residential purposes and forming part of a building from some other part of which it is divided horizontally.

Gallery A raised area or platform around the sides or at the back of a room which provides extra space.

Habitable room A room used, or intended to be used, for dwellinghouse purposes (including; for the purposes of Part B, a kitchen, but not a bathroom).

Height (of a building or storey for the purposes of Part B) Height of the top storey above ground is measured as shown in Appendix C, Diagram C1.

Inner room Room from which escape is possible only by passing through another room (the access room).

Material of limited combustibility A material performance specification that includes non-combustible materials, and for which the relevant test criteria are set out in Appendix A, paragraph 9.

Means of escape Structural means whereby [in the event of fire] a safe route or routes is or are provided for persons to travel from any point in a building to a place of safety.

Non-combustible material The highest level of reaction to fire performance. The relevant test criteria are set out in Appendix A, paragraph 8.

Notional boundary A boundary presumed to exist between buildings on the same site (see Section 9, Diagram 18).

Occupancy type A purpose group identified in Appendix D.

Pipe (for the purposes of Section 7) Includes pipe fittings and accessories; and excludes a flue pipe and a pipe used for ventilating purposes (other than a ventilating pipe for an above around drainage system).

Places of special fire hazard Oil-filled transformer and switch gear rooms, boiler rooms, storage space for fuel or other highly flammable substances, and rooms housing a fixed internal combustion engine.

Protected circuit An electrical circuit protected against fire.

Protected stairway A stair discharging through a final exit to a place of safety (including any exit passageway between the foot of the stair and the final exit) that is adequately enclosed with fire-resisting construction.

Purpose group A classification of a building according to the purpose to which it is intended to be put. See Appendix D, Table D1.

Relevant boundary The boundary which the side of the building faces, (and/or coincides with) and which is parallel, or at an angle of not more than 80°, to the side of the building (see Section 9 Diagram 17). A notional boundary can be a relevant boundary.

Rooflight A dome light, lantern light, skylight, ridge light, glazed barrel vault or other element intended to admit daylight through a roof.

Room (for the purposes of B2) An enclosed space within a building that is not used solely as a circulation space. (The term includes not only conventional rooms, but also walk-in cupboards that are not fittings, and large spaces such as warehouses and auditoria. The term does not include voids such as ducts, ceiling voids and roof spaces.)

Sheltered housing Includes:

a. two or more dwellings in the same building;

b. two or more dwellings on adjacent sites

where those dwellings are, in each case, designed and constructed for the purpose of providing residential accommodation for vulnerable or elderly people who receive, or who are to receive, a support service.

Single-storey building A building consisting of a ground storey only. (A separated part which consists of a ground storey only, with a roof to which access is only provided for repair or maintenance, may be treated as a single storey building.) Basements are not included in counting the number of storeys in a building.

Site (of a building) The land occupied by the building, up to the boundaries with land in other ownership.

Smoke alarm A device containing within one housing all the components, except possibly the energy source, necessary for detecting smoke and giving an audible alarm.

Self-closing device A device which is capable of closing the door from any angle and against any latch fitted to the door.

Storey includes:

a. any gallery if its area is more than half that of the space into which it projects; and

b. a roof, unless it is accessible only for maintenance and repair.

Storey exit A final exit, or a doorway giving direct access into a protected stairway, firefighting lobby or external escape route.

Suspended ceiling (fire-protecting) A ceiling suspended below a floor, which contributes to the fire resistance of the floor. Appendix A, Table A3, classifies different types of suspended ceiling.

Technical specification A standard or a European Technical Approval Guide. It is the document against which compliance can be shown in the case of a standard and against which an assessment is made to deliver the European Technical Approval.

Thermoplastic material See Appendix A, paragraph 17.

Unprotected area In relation to a side or external wall of a building means:

a. window, door or other opening; and

   Note: Windows that are not openable and are designed and glazed to provide the necessary level of fire resistance need not be regarded as an unprotected area.

b. any part of the external wall which has less than the relevant fire resistance set out in Section 8.

c. any part of the external wall which has combustible material more than 1mm thick attached or applied to its external face, whether for cladding or any other purpose. Combustible material in this context is any material which does not have a Class 0 rating.)

Appendix F: Standards and other publications referred to

Standards

DD 252:2002
Components for residential sprinkler systems. Specification and test methods for residential sprinklers

BS EN ISO 306:2004
Plastics. Thermoplastic materials. Determination of Vicat softening temperature (VST)

BS 476-3:2004
Fire tests on building materials and structures. Classification and method of test for external fire exposure to roofs

BS 476-4:1970
Fire tests on building materials and structures. Non-combustibility test for materials

BS 476-6:1989
Fire tests on building materials and structures. Method of test for fire propagation for products

BS 476-7:1997
Fire tests on building materials and structures. Method of test to determine the classification of the surface spread of flame of products

BS 476-8:1972
Fire tests on building materials and structures. Test methods and criteria for the fire resistance of elements of building construction (withdrawn)

BS 476-11:1982
Fire tests on building materials and structures. Method for assessing the heat emission from building materials

BS 476-20:1987
Fire tests on building materials and structures. Method for determination of the fire resistance of elements of construction (general principles)

BS 476-21:1987
Fire tests on building materials and structures. Methods for determination of the fire resistance of loadbearing elements of construction

BS 476-22:1987
Fire tests on building materials and structures. Methods for determination of the fire resistance of non-loadbearing elements of construction

BS 476-23:1987
Fire tests on building materials and structures. Methods for determination of the contribution of components to the fire resistance of a structure

BS 476-24:1987
Fire tests on building materials and structures. Method for determination of the fire resistance of ventilation ducts

BS EN 771-1:2003
Specification for masonry units. Clay masonry units

BS EN ISO 1182:2002
Reaction to fire tests for building products. Non-combustibility test

ENV 1187:2002+A1:2005, test 4
Test methods for external fire exposure to roofs

BS EN ISO 1716:2002
Reaction to fire tests for building products. Determination of the heat of combustion

BS 5438:1989
Methods of test for flammability of textile fabrics when subjected to a small igniting flame applied to the face or bottom edge of vertically oriented specimens

BS EN 14604:2005
Smoke alarm devices

BS 5446-2:2003
Fire detection and fire alarm devices for dwellings. Specification for heat alarms

BS 5839-1:2002
Fire detection and fire alarm systems for buildings. Code of practice for system design, installation, commissioning and maintenance

BS 5839-6:2004
Fire detection and fire alarm systems for buildings. Code of practice for the design, installation and maintenance of fire detection and fire alarm systems in dwellings

BS 5867-2:1980
Specification for fabrics for curtains and drapes. Flammability requirements

BS 7974:2001
Application of fire safety engineering principles to the design of buildings. Code of practice

BS 9251:2005
Sprinkler systems for residential and domestic occupancies. Code of practice

BS 8214:1990
Code of practice for fire door assemblies with non-metallic leaves

BS EN 1364-1:1999
Fire resistance tests for non-loadbearing elements. Walls

BS EN 1364-2:1999
Fire resistance tests for non-loadbearing elements. Ceilings

BS EN 1365-1:1999
Fire resistance tests for loadbearing elements. Walls

BS EN 1365-2:2000
Fire resistance tests for loadbearing elements. Floors and roofs

BS EN 1365-3:2000
Fire resistance tests for loadbearing elements. Beams

BS EN 1365-4:1999
Fire resistance tests for loadbearing elements. Columns

BS EN 1366-1:1999
Fire resistance tests for service installations. Ducts

BS EN 1366-2:1999
Fire resistance tests for service installations. Fire dampers

BS EN 1366-3:2004
Fire resistance tests for service installations. Penetration seals

BS EN 1366-4:2006
Fire resistance tests for service installations. Linear joint seals

BS EN 1366-5:2003
Fire resistance tests for service installations. Service ducts and shafts

BS EN 1366-6:2004
Fire resistance tests for service installations. Raised access and hollow core floors

BS EN 1634-1:2008
Fire resistance tests for door and shutter assemblies. Fire doors and shutters

BS EN 1634-2:2008
Fire resistance and smoke control tests for door and shutter assemblies, openable windows and elements of building hardware. Fire resistance characterisation test for elements of building hardware

BS EN 1634-3:2004
Fire resistance tests for door and shutter assemblies. Smoke control doors and shutters

BS EN ISO 11925-2:2002
Reaction to fire tests. Ignitability of building products subjected to direct impingement of flame. Single-flame source test

BS EN 13238:2001
Reaction to fire tests for building products. Conditioning procedures and general rules for selection of substrates

BS EN 13501-1:2007
Fire classification of construction products and building elements. Classification using test data from reaction to fire tests

BS EN 13501-2:2007
Fire classification of construction products and building elements. Classification using data from fire resistance tests, excluding ventilation services

BS EN 13501-3:2005
Fire classification of construction products and building elements. Classification using data from fire resistance tests on products and elements used in building service installations: fire resisting ducts and fire dampers

BS EN 13501-5:2005
Fire classification of construction products and building elements. Classification using data from external fire exposure to roof tests

BS EN 13823:2002
Reaction to fire tests for building products. Building products excluding floorings exposed to thermal attack by a single burning item

Publications

Legislation

Disability Discrimination Act 1995

Education Act 1996

Pipelines Safety Regulations 1996, SI 1996 No 825 and the Gas Safety (Installation and Use) Regulations 1998 SI 1998 No 2451

Electromagnetic Compatibility Regulations 1992 (SI 1992 No 2372)

Electromagnetic Compatibility (Amendment) Regulations 1994 (SI 1994 No 3080)

Electrical Equipment (Safety) Regulations 1994 (SI 1994 No 3260)

Commission Decision 2000/553/EC of 6th September 2000 implementing Council Directive 89/106/EEC

(European tests) Commission Decision 2000/367/EC of 3rd May 2000 implementing Council Directive 89/106/EEC

Commission Decision 2001/671/EC of 21 August 2001 implementing Council Directive 89/106/EC as regards the classification of the external fire performance of roofs and roof coverings

Commission Decision 2005/823/EC of 22 November 2005 amending Decision 2001/671/EC regarding the classification of the external fire performance of roofs and roof coverings

Commission Decision 2000/147/EC of 8th February 2000 implementing Council Directive 89/106/EEC

Commission Decision 2000/367/EC of 3rd May 2000 implementing Council Directive 89/106/EEC

Commission Decision 96/603/EC of 4th October 1996

94/61 1/EC implementing Article 20 of the Council Directive 89/106/EEC on construction products

Construction Products Regulations 1991 (SI 1991 No 1620)

Construction Product (Amendment) Regulations 1994 (SI 1994 No 3051)

The Workplace (Health, Safety and Welfare) Regulations 1992

Health and Safety (Safety signs and signals) Regulations 1996

Association for Specialist Fire Protection (ASFP)

ASFP Red book – *Fire stopping and penetration seals for the construction industry* 2nd Edition ISBN: 1 87040 923 X

ASFP Yellow book – *Fire protection for structural steel in buildings* 4th Edition ISBN: 1 87040 925 6

ASFP Grey book – *Fire and smoke resisting dampers* ISBN: 1 87040 924 8

ASFP Blue book – *Fire resisting ductwork* 2nd Edition ISBN: 1 87040 926 4

www.asfp.org.uk

The British Automatic Sprinkler Association (BAFSA)

Sprinklers for Safety: Use and Benefits of Incorporating Sprinklers in Buildings and Structures, (2006) ISBN: 0 95526 280 1

www.bafsa.org.uk

Building Research Establishment Limited (BRE)

BRE Digest 208 *Increasing the fire resistance of existing timber floors* 1988 ISBN: 978 1 86081 359 7

BRE report (BR 368) *Design methodologies for smoke and heat exhaust ventilation* 1999 ISBN: 978 1 86081 289 7

BRE report (BR 274) *Fire safety of PTFE-based materials used in buildings* 1994 ISBN: 978 1 86081 653 6

BRE report (BR 135) *Fire performance of external thermal insulation for walls of multi-storey buildings* 2003 ISBN: 978 1 86081 622 2

BRE report (BR 187) *External fire spread: Building separation and boundary distances* 1991 ISBN: 978 1 86081 465 5

BRE report (BR128) *Guidelines for the construction of fire resisting structural elements* 1988 ISBN: 0 85125 293 1

BRE 454 *Multi-storey timber frame buildings – a design guide* 2003 ISBN: 1 86081 605 3

www.bre.co.uk

Builders Hardware Industry Federation

Hardware for Fire and Escape Doors 2006 ISBN: 0 95216 422 1

www.firecode.org.uk

Department for Communities and Local Government

Regulatory Reform (Fire Safety) Order 2005 ISBN: 0 11072 945 5

Fire safety in adult placements: a code of practice

www.communities.gov.uk

Department for Education and Skills

Building Bulletin (BB) 100

www.dfes.gov.uk

Department of Health

HTM 05 – 02 *Guidance in support of functional provisions for healthcare premises*

www.dh.gov.uk

Door and Shutter Manufacturers' Association (DSMA)

Code of practice for fire-resisting metal doorsets 1999

www.dhfonline.org.uk

Environment Agency

Pollution Prevention Guidelines (PPG18) *Managing Fire Water and Major Spillages*

www.environment-agency.gov.uk

Football Licensing Authority

Concourses ISBN: 0 95462 932 9

www.flaweb.org.uk/home.php

Fire Protection Association (FPA)

Design guide

www.thefpa.co.uk

Glass and Glazing Federation (GGF)

A guide to best practice in the specification and use of fire-resistant glazed systems

www.ggf.org.uk

Health and Safety Executive (HSE)

Workplace health, safety and welfare, The Workplace (Health, Safety and Welfare) Regulations 1992, Approved Code of Practice and Guidance; The Health and Safety Commission, L24; published by HMSO 1992; ISBN: 0 11886 333 9

www.hse.gov.uk

International Association of Cold Storage Contractors (IACSC)

Design, construction, specification and fire management of insulated envelopes for temperature controlled environments 1999

www.iarw.org/iacsc/european_division

Passive Fire Protection Federation

Ensuring best practice for passive fire protection in buildings ISBN: 1 87040 919 1

www.pfpf.org

Steel Construction Institute (SCI)

SCI P197 Designing for structural fire safety:
A handbook for architects and engineers 1999
ISBN: 1 85942 074 5

SCI Publication 288 Fire safe design: A new
approach to multi-storey steel-framed buildings
(Second Edition) 2000 ISBN: 1 85942 169 5

SCI Publication P313 Single storey steel framed
buildings in fire boundary conditions 2002
ISBN: 1 85942 135 0

www.steel-sci.org

Timber Research and Development
Associations (TRADA)

Timber Fire-Resisting Doorsets: maintaining
performance under the new European test
standard ISBN: 1 90051 035 9

www.trada.co.uk

Index